THE PLANT HUNTERS

THE PLANT HUNTERS

CHARLES LYTE

ORBIS PUBLISHING, LONDON

This book is dedicated to my Mother, Constance Martha, a most loyal fan and constant supporter.

AUTHOR'S ACKNOWLEDGMENTS

This book would not have been possible but for the great help of the Chief Librarian of the Royal Botanic Gardens Library, Kew, Miss Sylvia Fitzgerald, the former Archivist, Miss Eirene Smith, and the Library staff. I am also greatly indebted to the staffs of the Royal Horticultural Society Library, the Royal Geographical Society Library, and the Natural History Museum Botany Library. I am grateful for the help I have received from Professor Philip F. Rehbeck, and Eleanor C. Au, both of the University of Hawaii; and special thanks must also go to the daughters of the late Frank Kingdon-Ward – Mrs Pleione Tooley, and Miss Martha Kingdon-Ward. Last, but by no means least, I must pay tribute to the patience and encouragement of my wife, Sarah, and my children.

Frontispiece: the Himalayan snowbeds at
13,000 feet, showing rhododendrons in blossom and
Mount Kangchenjunga in the distance. This illustration was used as
the frontispiece for Joseph Hooker's
Himalayan Journal.

© 1983 by Orbis Publishing Limited
First published in Great Britain by
Orbis Publishing Limited, London 1983

Printed in Great Britain
ISBN 0-85613-418-X.

CONTENTS

INTRODUCTION

When a garden is ablaze with flowers it is, with some justification, the gardener who receives the praise. But few of us give much, if any, thought to how those wonderful shrubs and trees, annuals and climbers, have come to be flourishing in cultivation, and still less to the people who discovered the parents of the species and hybrids which give us so much pleasure. Most of the plants that enrich our gardens are so familiar that we do not give them a second thought; it is as if the roses, lupins, lilies, pansies, primulas, geraniums, azaleas, rhododendrons, paeonies and other plants we take for granted have always been there.

However, if it had not been for the daring and endurance of a small band of dedicated men, these plants would probably be unknown to gardeners today, still a secret from the world in the fastnesses of mountain or jungle. And it is only because the names of those who searched for and found them have been given to the plants they discovered – Forestii, Wilsonii, Fortunei and Douglasiana, for example – that they are at all familiar.

Plants have been traded and passed from hand to hand since ancient times, and so it is virtually impossible to credit any one person with being the first plant hunter. In the beginning, the important plants were those with medicinal virtues or those that played a part in religious rituals. The ancient Egyptians sent out expeditions to collect the trees that produced a resin which they burned in temples. More recently, wealthy Chinese sent men deep into the forest in Yunnan to cut and bring home the fragrant and enduring wood of *Taiwania cryptomerioides,* which they used for making coffins. The delicately flavoured scorzonera, now eaten as a vegetable, was once regarded as a sovereign remedy for snake bite; and there is a story of a Moor in Spain who kept secret the place where it grew wild so that he could sell the roots at a large profit (though eventually he was followed and the plant was collected).

Even though plant collecting for food and medicine dates back to ancient civilizations, and doubtless reaches into a darker and more distant past, John Tradescant in the seventeenth century was probably the first man to hunt for plants in an organized way, and his story and those of several others who came after him are the subject of this book. Their tales are full of adventure and the dangers, discomforts and accidents that overtook them in the wilderness as they searched for plants, which were not merely those that were to ornament our gardens and parks, but also those that became the source of health-restoring and life-saving drugs, food and the raw materials of industry.

By the early eighteenth century, botany had become an increasingly important science, but one that was in a considerable state of chaos. New plants were being introduced to Europe and named by scientists, but in such an uncoordinated manner that dialogue between botanists was extremely difficult, if not impossible. It took Carl Linnaeus, born in 1707 in Sweden, to bring order to the naming of plants. His work at the University of Uppsala led to what is known as the Linnaean system, which has remained the basis of naming plants to this day. In his lifetime Linnaeus classified and named nearly 8000 different plants, and greatly simplified the task of identification for the field botanist, who would often have to return hundreds of miles to a plant seen in bloom earlier in the year, to gather its seed.

The eighteenth century saw the arrival of the professional plant hunter, a profession that grew throughout the nineteenth century and well into the first half of the twentieth. Britain produced the most successful men in the field, because they were backed by the great botanic gardens of Kew and Edinburgh, the Royal Horticultural Society, nursery gardens and wealthy patrons, and had the added advantage of the huge area of the British Empire in which to work. They all had in common a love of plants so great that they were willing to risk all kinds of dangers and diseases in order to experience the excitement of discovering something new, rare and beautiful. Profit was not the motive: for many years the salaries paid by the main employers of the collectors, the Botanic Gardens at Kew and the Royal Horticultural Society, were fixed at £100 a year; and there was no copyright on new plant introductions.

Mostly the plant hunters travelled alone, or with only one or two native servants to guide them and act as interpreters. Others, like Joseph Rock, assembled huge caravans, while George Forrest trained teams of local collectors so that he could cover a very large area. But nothing could be left to chance, and the plant hunter had personally to supervise the preparation of herbarium specimens, the drying and cleaning of seeds, the careful packing of the harvest for the long journey home, and the writing of detailed field notes. When the porters fell ill, the plant collector had to be doctor and nurse, when quarrels broke out he had to be referee and judge, and when the expeditions came under attack he had to be both general and troops. And always the plant hunter was at the mercy of the weather, sun and storm alike, and often the victim of abuse and assault.

The stories of these men who dared the wilderness have not been widely told. Once known, however, they seem to enhance and illuminate a garden. To look at a plant and know who found and collected it, and where and how, and of the dangers and difficulties he overcame to reach some hidden gorge in the Himalayas, or a corner of the lush jungle of the Amazon, or some searing waste in Australia, or snake-infested valley in Africa, does enrich the pleasure of having grown it. It is to be hoped that readers of this book will, when they see a plant in bloom, add to their enjoyment of it when they think of the intrepid plant hunters who braved the remote wild regions of the world to find the flowers now so much enjoyed in our gardens.

JOHN TRADESCANT (?-1638) & JOHN TRADESCANT THE YOUNGER (1608-62)

Perhaps the most accurate definition of a plant hunter is one who seeks to discover and collect plants unknown in his own country, regardless of their economic or ornamental value, collecting out of a simple love of plants for their own sake. John Tradescant was just such a man, although he did extend his collecting to all kinds of other curiosities of nature. He was one of the first true gardener-botanists, who, with their feel for both science and beauty, make the best plant collectors.

A Londoner, Tradescant came from a family who had been landowners in Suffolk before selling up and moving south. It seems likely that the Tradescants, their roots still firmly in the soil, started a nursery garden in or near London, and it was there that John was trained. He was clearly an apt pupil: as a young man in 1609 he became gardener to Sir Robert Cecil, the first Lord Salisbury, and was charged with laying out the gardens of Hatfield House. Later he became gardener to the Duke of Buckingham, Charles Villiers; and finally King Charles I appointed him Keeper of His Majesty's Garden.

When he was hired by Lord Salisbury, gardening in Britain was moving into a new phase. The growing prosperity of the Elizabethan age was producing a rash of great house building, and with it the laying out of splendid, if rather formal, pleasure gardens. To match the richness of the age, the wealthy vied with one another to have the most varied and exotic plants in their gardens. At that time, the number of interesting plants available in Britain was limited, though occasionally, and in a somewhat haphazard manner, new plants were brought into the country by seafarers. Cecil was encouraging a more orderly system of collecting when he sent John Tradescant to Europe to find rarities and novelties.

On his first trip, to France and Holland, Tradescant concentrated his search in nursery gardens where he bought large numbers of fruiting trees and bushes, as well as lime and sycamore trees for the broad avenues of the Cecil estate. The journey gave him a taste for travelling, and aroused an enthusiasm for collecting the rare and extraordinary which never left him.

Russia was a country that intrigued him. It was distant, wild and strange – mysterious enough to draw him even without the tales he had heard of whole islands covered with roses. From all accounts it had a rich plant life, and if the gems described to him could survive the cruel winters of Russia, they must surely flourish in Britain. The first real contact with the country by Britain had been made only sixty years before, in 1553, when Sir Richard Chancellor, the great navigator, came ashore from his vessel, the *Edward Bonaventure,* near the mouth of the River Dvina on the White Sea. He was part of an expedition mounted by The Mystery, Company, and Fellowship of Merchant Adventurers for the Discovery of Unknown Lands, whose objective was to find a route to China and India by sailing northwards round Norway. Chancellor's arrival on the Russian coast was, therefore, more by accident than design.

The expedition's leader, Sir Hugh Willoughby, had been frozen to death, along with his crew, in the Russian winter, but Chancellor and his men survived and travelled to Moscow by sledge, where they were kindly received by Czar Ivan Vassilovitch. Chancellor gave the Czar an open letter from Edward VI to the rulers of any country the expedition might reach, which said that the expedition had been sent 'to regions previously unknown, in order to seek such things as we stand in need of, as well as to take to them from our country such things as they require'. It was the bones of the first trade agreement with Russia.

Since then, relations between the two countries had deteriorated. In 1567 Czar Ivan had sent two Russian merchants to London to buy precious stones for his treasury. He also proposed marriage to Queen Elizabeth, partly through the encouragement of Dr Elija (Elisaeus) Bomel, a German from Westphalia with a reputation as a mathematician and astrologer. He had made his way to Russia where he ingratiated himself with the Czar and, with astrological tables and mystifying mathematical calculations, persuaded him that he should seek Elizabeth's hand, convincing him that the Queen was younger and more beautiful than she was. Bomel talked Ivan into a number of hasty and foolish decisions, was at the same time engaged in a conspiracy against Russia with the kings of Poland and Sweden, and also managed to extort from all and sundry a great deal of money, which he repatriated to Westphalia by way of England. Eventually his treachery was discovered, and led him to a ghastly death by roasting. The Bomel affair proved to be a considerable setback for the English presence in Russia and her share in the valuable trade between the two countries, and relations were still strained when Tradescant got the opportunity to travel there, accompanying Sir Dudley Digges on a diplomatic mission to Archangel on the White Sea.

Tradescant had left the employ of the Salisbury family following the death of Lord Salisbury, and moved to Kent to work for Sir Edward Wotton who was developing a garden in Canterbury. Sir Dudley Digges was Wotton's neighbour, and Tradescant was 'lent' to him to help him lay out a new garden. The two men became close friends, and it was Sir Dudley who urged John to join him on the voyage to Russia, so that he could search for new plants.

On 3 June 1618, they left Gravesend aboard the *Diana* and sailed to Newcastle, the vessel's home port, where Tradescant was sent ashore to buy fresh supplies of beef, mutton and salmon. A month later they were within the Arctic Circle. They were able to marvel at the midnight sun before plunging into a dense fog that did not lift for four days. When the weather did clear, they found that the ship was sailing in the midst of a school of whales. Tradescant recorded in his journal: 'The 5 of July we saw many whalls swim here by the ship.'

He busied himself trapping the birds that flew aboard, killing and preserving them, and making notes and observations on everything he saw and the people he met. He was unimpressed by the Samoyeds, 'a miserable people, of small growth'. They were, he felt sure, the legendary people who were said to to have no heads because they 'commonly wear their clothes over head and shoulders'. They wore animal skins, were armed with bows and arrows, and were, he said, 'extreme beggers, not to be denied'.

While diplomatic exchanges were taking place between Sir Dudley and the Russians, Tradescant took a ship's boat and went ashore to botanize. His first discovery was a yellow cranberry. On another occasion he was given the use of an Imperial craft, to explore the islands of the Dvina Delta. He was taken to the fabled 'Rose Island', which lived up to its name, being smothered with single roses in full flower 'such like our sinoment rose (*Rosa cinnamomea*). And who have the sense of smelling say they be marvellous sweet . . .' (Poor Tradescant had no sense of smell, a fact which proved to be a positive blessing at least once, when the expedition met Lapland fishermen, who were dressed in virtually raw seal skins and did 'stink so filthily'. He alone could get close enough to talk to them.) Other botanical finds included *Veratrum album*, which he called hellebore, and which grew in profusion. He also collected four different conifers, recorded *Betula alba*, which he noted grew to a great height, and collected red, white and black currants, several different bilberries, strawberries, at least one geranium, and a giant form of sorrel. But of all his introductions none made a greater and more enduring impact than the larch, both as a graceful ornamental plant and a timber tree that is still of enormous value.

Early in August the expedition began to make for home. The journey was not without incident: crossing the bar at the mouth of the Dvina, the craft touched bottom, and was held fast for eight hours before floating free. Then, two days later, they sailed into contrary winds that held them back for two days, after which a thick fog arose, so dense that visibility was virtually non-existent, and the vessel was nearly sucked into a whirlpool and smashed on the rocks. In addition to all this, the ship was in poor condition and so when rain fell, which it did in torrents, it would pour into Tradescant's cabin, soaking his clothes and bedding and ruining part of his collection. The ship's boys stole and ate some of the berries he had collected, and brackish water killed a number of living specimens. It is remarkable that he had anything left when he finally came ashore at St Katharine's Dock next to the Tower of London.

The following year an expedition was being fitted out for the Mediterranean, to seek and destroy the notorious pirates who were making trading an increasingly dangerous and risky business. Most of the blame was laid on the Algerians, and in particular on Barbarossa the Turk who, it was said, reigned over the most vicious nest of pirates ever to sail the sea. (In fact Barbarossa was not nearly as bad as he was portrayed: he brought law and order to the country, and made the harbour of Algiers safe for merchant ships of all nations, but the great trading nations did not like him having so much control of the Mediterranean, and were looking for a way to break his power.) The real villains were in fact the Barbary corsairs who ranged up and down the coast, picking off merchantmen whenever they could, and a polyglot collection of pirates, including English gangs, who preyed on shipping both in the Channel and the Mediterranean.

Because Algiers was such a safe port, British merchants were reluctant to back the venture, although the Government wanted to stage a show of force to demonstrate that it was a power to be reckoned with in such a commercially important part of the world. It was not until 1621 that the expedition was finally organized. For Tradescant it was the chance of a lifetime.

He had heard of a fabulous apricot that grew in Algiers and he dearly wanted to bring it to England; and he also longed to collect from the rich flora of the Mediterranean coast. He therefore rallied to the flag and joined up as a gentleman volunteer. At first his application was not taken seriously, particularly when he suggested he might make a good gunner, but in the end, to his delight, he was taken on.

The expedition was extremely successful from a plant collector's point of view, although from a military and political standpoint it appears to have been something of a disappointment. Tradescant certainly found his Algerian apricot, in fact he collected two varieties, but his haul was clearly a great deal larger than this. Mea Allan, in *The Tradescants,* her detailed biography of John Tradescant and his son, gives a list of Mediterranean plants not introduced to Britain before 1621. It therefore seems reasonable to suppose that a great many of them were collected by Tradescant while he was engaged on his apparently not very burdensome military duties. He certainly introduced *Gladiolus byzantinus,* now naturalized in some parts of Britain, lilac (*Syringa persica*), narcissus, crocus, colchicum, cistus, lychnis, jasmine and very many other plants.

Five years after the expedition, Tradescant set up home with his family in South Lambeth and proceeded to establish a garden that became of great botanical importance. His house became a museum, based on his 'Closett of Rarities', which included not only items that he himself had collected on his wanderings, but curiosities brought to him by other travellers.

Tradescant's passion for gardens and plants, and his unflagging zeal for collecting artefacts and the curiosities of nature was passed on to his son, John the younger. With such a background it was probably inevitable that young John, who had been a scholar at King's School (Kings College), Canterbury, should follow in his father's footsteps and search the world for wonders, but, unlike his father, he chose the New World. In 1637, at the age of twenty-nine, he sailed for Virginia, and it was officially recorded that he was in the colony 'to gather all rarities of flowers, plants, shells, etc.'. And this he did, both on that occasion and again when he returned in 1642 and 1654; and during his voyages he collected in the West Indies.

The plants he sent home to his father in South Lambeth have transformed British parks and gardens. He collected the black locust or false acacia, *Robinia pseudoacacia,* a fine tree that now flourishes all over Europe, *Lilium canadense,* a beautiful yellow lily and a plantsman's favourite ever since it was introduced, *Tradescantia virginiana,* with its wonderful blue flowers, which helps keep the Tradescant family name alive, *Oenothera biennis,* the handsome, tall, yellow evening primrose that has since become naturalized as a wayside plant, and *Liriodendron tulipifera,* the magnificent and graceful tulip tree.

One tree in particular is an outstanding memorial to both father and son. It is the London plane, which owes its existence to their tireless collecting. It is a cross between *Platanus orientalis* and *Platanus occidentalis. Platanus orientalis* was already growing in the South Lambeth garden when John the younger sent home the seeds of *Platanus occidentalis.* The new plane tree was planted next to the old, eventually the two crossed, and their offspring, *Platanus acerifolia* – the London plane – became the parent of generations of fine street trees which have survived blitz and pollution to be as familiar a part of the capital city as the changing of the guard at Buckingham Palace.

History has not treated the Tradescants kindly. They have been portrayed merely as gardeners to the rich and powerful, when, in fact, they helped to lay the foundation for the more scientific botanical collecting of later years. They introduced new colour, form and variety to European gardens, and established one of the first great museums, the Ashmolean in Oxford. Credit for the latter was taken from them by Elias Ashmole who, in the pursuit of self-aggrandizement, tricked John Tradescant's widow out of the collection of curiosities at Lambeth, took them for himself, and represented them to the world as the museum that bears his name. But however loathsome the chicanery of Ashmole, what he could not claim for himself was the profession of plant explorer and collector, established by the Tradescants and followed by botanists for the next three hundred years.

SIR JOSEPH BANKS
(1743-1820)

If John Tradescant the Elder (see Chapter 1) was the founding father of plant collectors, then Sir Joseph Banks was definitely the man who turned plant hunting into a profession. A man of great energy, daring, and exceptional organizational ability, he played a prominent part in bringing science out of the maze of myth and superstition into the more pragmatic atmosphere of the laboratory. His greatest passion, botany, dominated his long, full life.

Banks was born in 1744 into wealth and privilege. His family owned large estates in Lincolnshire, and mining interests elsewhere in the country. His father died when Joseph was only seventeen, which meant that he had a large fortune at his disposal from a very early age. Not particularly academic, he had an unspectacular career at Harrow and Eton, and finally at Oxford, but it was while he was at Eton that he developed his great love for botany, receiving his first instruction from women who collected wild plants from the hedgerows to supply the herbalists. At Oxford he had to import his own botany teacher, because Dr Humphrey Sibthorp, who occupied the Chair of Botany, had only delivered one lecture in thirty-five years and had no intention of giving another for any wealthy yeoman.

When young Joseph inherited his great fortune it was expected that, like other young men in his position, he would make the Grand Tour of Europe to add the final polish to his education. To everyone's surprise and horror, however, he announced his intention of going to Labrador and Newfoundland to study and collect plants, and also birds, mammals, fish, insects and minerals; indeed, anything that came to hand was to be collected. It was a bleak and dangerous part of the world, and his family concluded that he had taken leave of his senses. Despite having great pressure exerted on him to change his mind, he took passage in a naval fisheries protection vessel, which was sailing to the cod banks to keep the peace between the French and English fishermen, and spent about nine months in the territory, where he made the first major collection of plants from that region and served his apprenticeship as a field botanist.

In his absence he was elected a Fellow of the Royal Society, which was to have a commanding influence on his career. With the germ of travel now in his blood he was soon restless after returning to England, and in May 1767 he set out on a journey through the West Country, Wales, and the northwest of England, collecting plants and studying everything from canal digging to fossils.

When he arrived back in London, talk of a major expedition to Tahiti in the South Seas was already causing excitement. The aim of the venture was to observe the transit of Venus which, it was thought, would help to make navigation more accurate and was to be a joint undertaking between the Navy and the Royal Society. A voyage to Tahiti with all the stops along the way – Madeira, Rio de Janeiro, Tierra del Fuego – would have been satisfying enough for the Royal Society and the Admiralty, but Cook had special orders from the Crown to sail on from Tahiti after observing the transit of Venus, to seek out Terra Australis Incognita, the Unknown Southern Land. Geographers were convinced that there must be a great continent in the Southern Hemisphere to compensate for the huge land mass of the Northern Hemisphere. Without it, many argued, the world could not possibly be balanced. The land that Tasman had seen in 1642, and which appeared on eighteenth-century maps rather like the fading grin of the Cheshire Cat, was widely supposed to be the edge of Terra Australis Incognita. (It was in fact part of the western coastline of New Zealand.) Naturally enough, wishful thinking vested the continent with unimaginable riches. For the British Government it was an opportunity for colonial expansion and domination of the Pacific, and they were ambitious to get there before France or Spain. Cook was therefore told to settle finally the mystery of the Southern Continent, or of any other land that might lie in that hemisphere and, having discovered it, to hammer the Union Jack firmly into its soil.

Banks persuaded the Royal Society to back him as the official naturalist on the expedition. All he wanted was a passage for himself and his party, whose expenses he would meet out of his own pocket. The offer was accepted, and in August 1768 he, along with the naturalist Dr Daniel Solander (who had been trained by the great plant classifier Carl Linnaeus) and three artists, Sydney Parkinson, John Reynolds and Alexander Buchan, as well as two servants, James Roberts and Peter Briscoe, boarded the *Endeavour*, commanded by Captain James Cook, and sailed for Tahiti.

Apart from causing seasickness, from which Banks suffered miserably, particularly when the flat-bottomed vessel tended to roll heavily, the voyage was uneventful until they reached Tierra del Fuego, the tip of South America. There he and a party went ashore in harsh weather conditions, and were trapped in a blizzard in which two men died.

Early in April 1769 they anchored in Matavai Bay, Tahiti, and for the next five months Banks could delight in the marvellous tropical vegetation, which he and Dr Solander most assiduously collected and recorded, and which the artists copied in a wonderful series of paintings. He also developed a new and absorbing interest in primitive peoples, discovering that he was able to establish strong contacts, and was increasingly used by Cook as the intermediary between him and the native populations they met during the remainder of the voyage.

In August they left the island and headed deep into the

Pacific. On 6 October the look-out sighted land. It was New Zealand. They approached and landed and, in spite of regular brushes with Maoris, who did not welcome the strangers, Cook was able to establish that New Zealand was two islands and not part of the coast of the Southern Continent. Banks made a considerable collection of plants, and observed that the land seemed ideal for settling and for supplying plenty of materials 'either for the building of defences, houses or vessels'.

In early 1770 they left New Zealand and again headed into virtually unknown seas. The ship's company, growing tired of the voyage, was depressed by the fact that Cook had proved New Zealand to be a country in its own right, and began to doubt that Terra Australis Incognita existed at all. Most of those on board wanted to go home, and during the night watches deliberately altered course. Banks became impatient with this defeatist attitude; Cook merely readjusted the course. On 19 April the coast of New South Wales was at last sighted, and after an initial disappointment with what appeared to be seared and wretched terrain, Banks recorded in his journal:

> The country this morn rose in gentle sloping hills which had the appearance of the highest fertility, every hill seemed to be clothed with trees of no mean size.

Sailing northwards, they found no harbour until the end of April, when they went ashore at Botany Bay, aptly named by Banks for its prodigal wealth of plants which kept him and Solander happy and busy for days. Of all the landfalls they visited, this was the most memorable to the naturalists.

A month later they were weaving their way through the Great Barrier Reef when, at supper time on 10 June, the *Endeavour* abruptly ran aground. Since they had already scraped over so many reefs, this one was judged to be no more than the tail end of a shoal. Banks entered in his journal:

> We went to bed in perfect security, but scarce were we warm in our beds when we were called up with the alarming news of the ship being fast upon a rock, which she in

a few moments convinced us of by beating very violently against the rocks. Our situation became now greatly alarming . . . All this time she continued to beat very much so that we could hardly keep our legs upon the quarter deck; by the light of the moon we could see her sheating boards etc., floating thick round her; about twelve her false keel came away.

The vessel began taking on water, and the entire company, including Banks, was put to work at the pumps. In the heat of the following day, as one man took over from another, the relieved man would collapse on the deck, only to be revived by the water flowing from the pumps. Eventually the leak was contained by a fother (a sheet of canvas tufted with oakum) which was sucked into the hole in the hull, and stemmed the flow of water long enough for the ship to be dragged off the coral by teams of oarsmen in the ship's boats.

Three days later they found a safe harbour in the mouth of a river, today called the Endeavour river, where it was possible to haul down the craft and carry out repairs. The hole was big enough to have sunk a ship with much more power-ful pumps; what saved them was a large lump of coral which had broken off in the gash and partly blocked it. Banks and Solander used this time usefully to botanize, although they were threaten-ed by the Aborigines, and it was here that they shot their first kangaroo. Banks examined it and declared that 'to compare it to any European animal would be impossible, as it has not the least resemblance to any one I have seen'. After the examination it was eaten and 'proved excellent meat', supplemented with turtles, 'far preferable to any I have eaten in England'. Un-fortunately, relationships with the Aborigines deteriorated during the time they had to spend repairing the Endeavour, and came to a head when a party of them tried to set fire to tents and equipment on the beach.

On 4 August they left the harbour, but it took nine anxiety-filled days to reach the safety of the open sea. On 16 August they returned to the Great Barrier Reef and, caught in the huge swell, were sucked towards the coral once again, and only saved by the ebbing tide. It was not until ten days later that they broke free from the reef. Now they began to sail for New Guinea and the Dutch East Indies where they were to take on fresh supplies and make more permanent repairs. Unfortunately, disease was rife in the Dutch East Indies, and more men were lost as a result of the stay at Batavia (present-day Djakarta) than throughout the entire circumnavigation of the globe. The journey home was broken at Cape Town, where Banks was deeply impressed by the wonderful flora of the Cape of Good Hope, and at the island of St Helena. On 12 July 1771 he once again set foot on English soil, when he came ashore at Deal.

London lionized him on his return, and he began laying plans to accompany Captain Cook on a second voyage round the world. His schemes came to nothing, however, when he quarrelled with the Admiralty over the alterations to the *Resolution* that he demanded to accommodate his very much larger party. Angered and somewhat humiliated, he chartered a yacht and cruised through the Western Islands to Iceland. It was the last of his expeditions.

By now a close friend of King George III, he became unofficial Director of the Royal Botanic Gardens at Kew (then a property of the Crown), which he developed into a major international botanical and seed-clearing centre. His home in Soho Square, which housed a remarkable library and ever-growing herbarium, became a focus for scientific debate, and at Spring Grove, his small country estate outside London, he conducted experiments in growing rice and blueberries.

From his own experience he realized that it was quite impracticable to depend on an uncertain trickle of seeds and dried plants from amateurs, and that experienced professionals had to be sent out into the field. The first of these collectors was Francis Masson (see Chapter 3), whom he sent to South Africa. He also assisted Archibald Menzies, who sent home seed of the monkey puzzle tree (*Araucaria araucana*); John Ledyard, who collected in Kamchatka; William Hooker, who went to Iceland; and Dr Clarke Abel, who gathered roses and lilies in China. He advised and supported a great number of other collectors, such as Allan Cunningham (see Chapter 4), and gave encouragement to young botanists like James Edward Smith, whom he persuaded to buy the herbarium, library and collections of the great plant classifier Carl Linnaeus in 1783. Altogether Banks was responsible for the introduction into England of more than 7000 new plant species; and he set a style of plant hunting which kept British collectors in the forefront of botanical discovery for many years. The Australian genus *Banksia,* which comprises more than forty species of evergreen shrubs and trees, is named after him.

FRANCIS MASSON
(1741-1805)

The successful circumnavigation of the world by Captain Cook (1768-71), and the strong scientific flavour of the voyage, for which Banks was largely to be credited, heightened interest in all things new and exotic, not least plants. It was quite clear to Banks that if the flowering treasures of the world were to be gathered, a more orderly, professional approach had to be adopted; no longer was it enough to depend on the curiosity or goodwill of sailors, travellers and embassies abroad. Banks and his team had proved that a systematic and scientific approach paid off, but because of the nature of his voyage round the world he had been able to bring back only relatively few seeds, with the bulk of his collections being herbarium specimens, that is, dried plants for cataloguing. What was now needed was to equip and finance a collector to go to a particular area in order to collect the living plants, bulbs, roots and seeds of the region and ship them back to Britain with the least delay.

In his position as unofficial Director of Kew Gardens, Banks was able to persuade George III of the value of such an expedition, urging that South Africa, whose rich flora he had glimpsed on his return from Australia, was the right location for the first Kew plant-hunting venture. The man he was looking for to become Kew's first professional collector had to be tough, resourceful, intelligent, have a reasonable understanding of

botany, a keen eye for a good plant and, above all, the skills of a
first-rate gardener. He found his man in Francis Masson, who
was employed at Kew. Masson had been born and brought up in
Aberdeen where, after a basic formal education, he was apprenticed as a garden boy. Later he made his way to London where
he found employment as a gardener in the Royal Botanic
Gardens, and at the same time he taught himself botany and
became a skilful botanical draughtsman.

The expedition to South Africa fitted in with the start of
Cook's second great voyage round the world, and Masson was
given a berth in the *Resolution* as far as Cape Town. He travelled
with the expedition naturalists, Johann Reinhold Forster and
his son Johann George Adam Forster, who arrogantly dis-
missed Masson as merely a 'Scots garden hand'. When Masson
later published a report of his journeys, Forster senior remarked:

> I have not yet come across a translation [into German]
> of this poor product, and if all our publishers, who are
> only to eager to print almost anything, really had projected
> it, then this would fully establish its value for our public,
> so we need not waste words over it.

Forster was an habitually jealous man who could not tolerate
anyone else enjoying success in the field of the natural sciences,
which he seemed to think was reserved exclusively for himself
and his son. What then would he have thought of the comments
of Sir James Edward Smith, the man who bought, and brought
to England, the library and collections of the great Carl Linnaeus, who gave order to scientific nomenclature? Writing in
Ree's Cyclopeadia in 1819, he said:

> The writer of this well recollects the pleasure which
> the novel sight of an African geranium (*Pelargonium*)
> in Yorkshire and Norfolk gave him about forty years
> ago. Now every garret and cottage window is filled with
> numerous species of that beautiful tribe, and every
> greenhouse glows with the innumerable bulbs, plants and
> splendid heaths of the Cape. For all these we are princi-
> pally indebted to Mr Masson.

Sir James was not exaggerating. During his African expeditions Masson collected a prodigious number of plants, such as *Pelargonium capitatum*, the marvellous scarlet *Erica cerinthoides*, tritonias, including *crocata* and *hyalina*, which will survive outdoors in mild areas, red-hot pokers and gladioli, all of which quite revolutionized gardening.

At the end of October 1772 Masson arrived in Cape Town, where he fell in with a Scandinavian mercenary, Franz Pehr Oldenburg, who had been in the service of the Dutch East India Company. Oldenburg was enterprising, practical and tough, and an ideal companion for Masson, who, after the tranquillity of Kew and with no experience of travelling and exploration, was now facing a harsh, sparsely colonized land. Oldenburg knew the country, spoke Dutch as well as some native dialects, and was certainly well qualified to see the Scotsman through his explorer's apprenticeship.

It was just outside Cape Town during those first few months in the colony that Masson came abruptly up against the violence and danger that were to be his constant companions throughout his plant-hunting career. He had set off alone for a day's botanizing, and was collecting on Table Mountain when he was spotted by a chain-gang of convicts who had escaped from their guards. It was late, and the brilliant, lavish sunset was swiftly followed by the velvety blackness of an African night. In the thorn bushes and acacia trees frogs whistled like birds; cries, shrill and low, menacing and frightened, filled the darkness as hunter and hunted engaged in the deadly business of survival. For Masson, though, the clank of chains and the harsh voices of angry men forcing their way through the tangle of grass and bushes were far more terrible sounds, which grew louder as the convicts came towards him, moving to and fro, trying to trap him to use as a hostage for their freedom. He was unarmed except for the clasp-knife he used for gathering specimens, and he knew enough of the rugged Dutch settlers to know they would sooner let him die than free the convicts. All night he crouched in terror in the undergrowth, and it was not until just before dawn that he was able to slip away to safety.

The first proper expedition began on 10 December the same year, but was little more than a jaunt compared with the journeys to come. They went to Stellenbosch by way of Paarl, then travelled east to Swartberg mountain before returning to Cape Town, stopping briefly at Swellendam on the way.

Back in Cape Town, Masson met a fellow botanist, Carl Peter Thunberg, who had been a pupil of Linnaeus at Uppsala in Sweden. The two men immediately became friends and decided to travel together deeper into the interior. It was an almost ideal partnership, with Thunberg providing the scientific expertise and Masson the horticultural skills and his gardener's eye for a fine plant. It would have been hard, however, to find two more disparate characters. Masson was modest almost to the point of being self-effacing, while Thunberg was a strutting, boastful man and, if his self-adulation had not been so comic, he could have been quite objectionable. His own accounts of his journeys always cast him in the role of the swashbuckling adventurer cheerfully ignoring all danger.

A typical example of this bragging was his version of the crossing of the Duvvenhoek's river. The two men had spent the night at a farmhouse, where they had been generously and kindly entertained by the farmer's wife. As it was the rainy season, the river, normally little more than a rivulet, had swollen into a dangerous flood. The woman sent an African with them to point out the fording point, but since she spoke no English, and neither of the botanists spoke Dutch, confusion and misunderstanding arose. Thunberg later claimed that the man pointed out a track to the right, when it should have been one to the left:

> I, who was the most courageous of any of the company, and, in the whole course of the journey, was constantly obliged to go on before and head them, now also, without a moment's consideration, rode plump into the river, until, in a moment, I sank with my horse into a large and deep sea-cow [hippo] hole, up to my ears. This would undoubtedly have proved my grave, if my horse had not by good luck been able to swim; and I, who have always

26

had the great good fortune to possess myself in the greatest dangers, had not, with the greatest calmness and composure, guided the animal (which floundered about violently in the water) and kept myself fast in the saddle, though continually lifted up by the stream. All this time my fellow travellers stood frightened on the opposite bank and astonished, without daring to trust themselves to an element that appeared so full of danger. However, as soon as I had got off my horse and let the water drain off me a little, I ordered my Hottentots to drive across the river according to a better direction that I gave them, after which the others followed.

Masson's version of events, while less colourful, has a more solid ring of truth than Thunberg's somewhat Munchausenian account:

The Doctor imprudently took the ford without the least enquiry; when on a sudden, he and his horse plunged over head and ears into a pit, that had been made by the *Hippopotamus amphibius*, which formerly inhabited these rivers. The pit was very deep, and steep on all sides, which made my companion's fate uncertain for a few minutes; but, after several strong exertions, the horse gained the opposite side with his rider.

The hippo pits, which had been enlarged and deepened by the animals over many generations, were a constant hazard, but the travellers saw few of the animals. By 1773, the year of Masson and Thunberg's first expedition, the Boer settlers had already made an impact on the land and its wildlife, and had virtually denuded the rivers of hippos which they shot for their flesh, and considered to be quite as good as pork.

Masson disapproved of this wholesale slaughter as much as he did of the way the Africans were treated. He observed that they were employed as servants, but only paid with beads and tobacco mixed with cannabis, which kept them more or less permanently drugged. 'A few free Hottentots still remain here, who live in their ancient manner; but are miserable wretches, having hardly any stock of cattle', he wrote in his journal. The settlers' lives were hardly luxurious, either: the land was hard to cultivate and no fortunes were made from it.

Continuing their journey, Masson and Thunberg struggled over the hills, and for three hours they had to lead their horses through torrential rain. The track was so slippery that the horses constantly slipped and stumbled, and their legs were cut and bleeding. The track led along the edge of precipices so steep that they dared not look over them. Eventually they reached Olyfant's river, where they came to a wretched settlement. In his journal, Masson wrote:

> Towards sunset, with great labour and anxiety, we got safe to the other side where we found a miserable cottage belonging to a Dutchman. Being however cold and wet, we were glad to take refuge under his roof. The hut had only one room; but our host gave us a corner to sleep in, which was detached by a hanging of reed mats, where he and his wife also slept; and in the other end lay a number of Hottentots promiscuously together.

The two men travelled in a kind of elliptical circle which took them over the Great Winterhock Mountain and through the Little Karoo, then known as Canaan's Land, back to Cape Town. It was a journey as rich in adventure as it was in botanical discovery: time after time they had to force their horses through rivers in full flood. The fierce contrasts in the terrain never failed to amaze Masson. Although the flooding waters of the Gouritz river reached their saddles, on either side the Karoo spread out, its red rocky soil burning, dry, almost too hot to touch; a desert but for the wonderfully adapted plants that grew so freely. It was there that they found a large number of new species of the succulent crassula and cotyledon, euphorbia, portulaca and mesembryanthemum. And when they crossed Van Staadens river they found themselves, by contrast, in a verdant country, made dangerous by the huge herds of African buffalo that grazed on the open land and sought shelter from the sun in the woods.

For more than four months they trekked through semi-desert,

over vast grasslands, clambering over mountains and crossing dangerous rivers. Alternately soaked by torrential rain and broiled by the intense sun, slogging over a landscape that despite its beauty seemed designed to break man, beast and waggon, and often half-starved, they found what they had come for – the superb plants which transformed the bush into what seemed like a riotous herbaceous garden, conceived and planted on a gargantuan scale. They found *Ixia viridiflora,* with its extraordinary blue-green flowers, and *Ixia cinnamomea, pilosa,* and *fucata,* all of which parented the brilliant-hued hybrids of today; *Protea,* now the national flower of South Africa, *Erythrina corallodendron* (the coral tree), and *Ornithogalum thyrsoides* (chincherinchee).

On their return to Cape Town, Masson was kept busy for weeks sorting out the collections, and preparing and packing them for shipment to England. For relaxation during this period, he and Thunberg collected in the country around the town, in the company of an energetic sixty-year-old, Lady Ann Monson, who had stopped at the colony on her way to India. Formerly Lady Ann Vane, she was, through her mother's family, the great-granddaughter of Charles II. Now married to a colonel in the service of the East India Company and a member of the Supreme Council of Bengal, Lady Ann was an accomplished botanist whose skill was recognized by Linnaeus, who named the genus *Monsonia* after her.

Towards the end of 1774 Masson and Thunberg started out on their second expedition together. The weather was intensely hot and dry, and the country they travelled through was little more than desert. The arid, sandy soil was made all the more treacherous by being undermined by mole-rats, whose network of tunnels was so deep that the horses sank into the earth up to their shoulders every six or seven minutes. Even worse, however, were the snakes which infested the dry, stony region. Fleeing for safety from the travellers, the snakes wriggled between the horses' legs, and when the two explorers rested during the heat of the day the serpents would slither over their bodies, sometimes even pausing to rest on them. Remarkably, neither man was bitten, not even when Thunberg woke to find a snake wrapped round his leg.

Less than a month after leaving the comforts of Cape Town, they nearly came to grief while crossing a stretch of the Karoo on their way to the Roggeveld Mountains. It was a three-day journey with no source of fresh water, and the only way to preserve the lives of the oxen hauling their waggons was to find the few pools of brackish water that existed off the main track. A Boer farmer and his family, travelling ahead of them on the same route, had promised to tie markers to the trees close to where there was water, but by the end of the first day there was no sign of a marker.

Throughout the next day they moved slowly under the relentless sun. Weakened for want of water, the wretched oxen simply lay down in their harness, and had to be prodded and beaten to their feet. If they stopped, Masson and Thunberg knew they were finished. They had to confine their collecting to the plants growing by the side of the track, but even so they found over a hundred fine specimens.

Although he forgot to mark the water holes, the farmer did send out a fresh team of oxen to meet the exhausted party, and it helped to haul their waggons up the mountains at the edge of the Little Karoo. They began the ascent when the day began to cool, but the way was so rugged that it took five Africans hanging on to ropes to prevent each waggon overturning. Descending was even more dangerous. Describing one descent in his journal, Masson wrote:

> We were furnished with fresh oxen, and several Hotten-tots, who, with long thongs of leather affixed to the upper part of our waggons, kept them from overturning, while we were obliged to make both the hind wheels fast with an iron chain to retard their motion. After two and a half hours employed in hard labour, sometimes pulling on one side, sometimes on the other, and sometimes all obliged to hang on with all our strength behind the waggon, to keep it from running over the oxen, we arrived at the foot of the mountain, where we found the heat more troublesome than the cold had been at the top.

While the two botanists received a great deal of kindness and hospitality from the white farmers, Masson was constantly shocked and angered by the way they treated the Africans. One day he met an armed band of Dutchmen who told him that they had been hunting and killing natives, who, they claimed, had killed their shepherds and stolen hundreds of sheep. But Masson's own observations of the natives, bushmen, he called them, in the Roggeveld, certainly did not match the claims of the settlers. He found them a simple, nomadic people who survived by scavenging and hunting, using bows and arrows poisoned with a mixture of snake venom and the sap from a euphorbia. They had no flocks or herds, lived in caves and crevices among the rocks, and ate roots, snakes, lizards and even scorpions, as well as caterpillars and ants' eggs.

Masson and Thunberg returned to Cape Town battered but triumphant, and with a superb collection of plants, having survived some of the roughest country in the world. By the end of 1775 Masson had returned to London. His success had exceeded even Banks's most ambitious hopes, and he was welcomed into the company of the most learned men of the time. However, despite the fulsome praise loaded upon him he remained a modest, unassuming man.

Thunberg and a number of other botanists wanted him to allow a plant he had discovered to be named after him, but he would not permit this without the permission of Linnaeus. In a letter to the great man, dated 26 December 1775, he wrote:

The enclosed specimen I think is a new genus, to which my worthy friend, Dr Thunberg, had the great desire of giving the name of Massonia, honouring me with this mark of his friendship. But notwithstanding the goodwill of Dr Thunberg, and many other botanical friends, I had declined receiving that honour from any other authority than the great Linnaeus, who I look upon as the father of botany and natural history, in hopes that you will give it your sanction. I am sorry that the leaves are not more perfect; but it is the only specimen I have. I shall take the liberty of giving a description of the roots and leaves . . .

31

For Masson, working at Kew again was tedious after his explorations of South Africa and discovery of its virtually untouched flora, so in 1778 Banks sent him abroad again, to collect in Madeira, Tenerife, the Western Isles (the Azores) and the Spanish Main. He made important collections at the first three stops, but did not reach the Spanish Main. Instead, he went to the islands of Barbados, Antigua, St Eustatius, St Christopher, Nevis, St Lucia and Grenada.

It was while he was on Grenada that a French force attacked the island, and he was drafted into the local militia, and captured fighting in the trenches. The horror of imprisonment haunted him for the rest of his life, and perhaps for the first time he appreciated the motives of the chain-gang which had hunted him through the African bush. Eventually he was released, but his West Indian expedition was fraught with difficulties which, in the end, drove him back to England. Almost all his valuable collections were spoiled or partly destroyed by being held up waiting for a ship to get them home, and on St Lucia he lost virtually everything in a hurricane.

Once again, work as a gardener at Kew, however distinguished, became irksome, and he turned to Sir Joseph for help. Banks liked and admired Masson; after all, the 'Scots garden hand' had proved correct his argument that it was eminently worthwhile sending trained men overseas to search for new plants. He wrote a memorandum to the King supporting Masson's request for another commission, pointing out that it was due to his collections that

> Kew Gardens has in great measure attained to that acknowledged superiority which it now holds over every similar establishment in Europe; some of which, as Trianon, Paris, Uppsala etc., till lately vied with each other for pre-eminence, without allowing even a competition from any English garden.

He added that Masson was now among the most respected men 'with all those who make natural history their study or amusement'. After ten years' experience in the field, this tireless worker had developed into a fine botanist, and Banks wrote:

> I am confident that the famous journey to the Levant
> made by M. Tournefort, by the order of Louis XIV at
> an immense expense, did not produce a greater addition
> of plants to the Paris Gardens, as Mr Masson's voyage
> to the Cape only has done to that at Kew.
>
> As far as I am able to judge, His Majesty's appointment
> to Mr Masson is to be accounted among the few Royal
> bounties which have not been in any degree misapplied.

Certainly Masson was no great drain on the royal purse.
He was paid a salary of £100 a year, a payment which became
fixed for plant collectors for many years to come, and expenses
which were not allowed to exceed £200, except under the most
extraordinary circumstances.

War with France considerably hampered new expeditions,
and it was not until 16 October 1785 that Masson left for his
second voyage to the Cape. He arrived in Table Bay on 10
January 1786, on the *Earl of Talbot,* a vessel of the British East
India Company. Once ashore, he found that conditions in the
colony had changed markedly since his last visit, as a consequence of the attempt by a British expeditionary force to
annexe the Cape in 1781. The force had launched an attack at
Saldanha Bay and captured and towed away a number of Dutch
East Indiamen. As so often happened to plant collectors, Masson
found himself caught up in a sensitive political situation, with
every Englishman now regarded with the greatest suspicion.
As a result, visiting foreigners were restricted to Cape Town
and only a few miles around it. Masson felt hemmed in and ill
at ease, so he suggested that he should ship on to India where he
would have more freedom. The request was turned down.

He had a letter of introduction from the Dutch Ambassador
in London, D. W. Van Lijnden, and a request from the Marquis
of Carmarthen, the British Minister for Foreign Affairs, urging
the authorities to give him permission to collect plants, but it
took a considerable time for the Governor to issue his approval,
and even then it was the most restricted permission. According

33

to a resolution of the Council, dated 17 January 1786, the curbs on his movements were:

> that all opportunities are to be denied to approach the sea coasts within a distance of three hours' journeying [from Cape Town]; and to allow to the same [Masson] abundant scope for researching and collecting notable herbs and plants on all regions and mountains that lie within the defined limits; provided that also the mountains within the said extreme limits may only be visited and traversed along their lower landward slopes.

If Masson took a step over the limits laid down, he was to be arrested by anyone, civilian or official, and brought back at his own expense to Cape Town, where his travel documents would be confiscated.

The restrictions were unbearably limiting and Masson very largely ignored them, making a number of trips over the years which were well beyond the prescribed limits, to collect plants. These he brought on in a small garden in Cape Town, before shipping them to Britain. But the suspicion and mistrust surrounding him had a deleterious effect, and this second, and last, South African expedition did not repeat the spectacular successes of the first.

Eventually, in 1795, he returned home to England once more and, having seen his plants safely settled in Kew, began again to grow restless. In the autumn of 1797 he set sail for North America, and on 8 November the look-out spotted three ships bearing down on the lone British vessel. One, a French pirate, opened fire with cannon and small arms, before boarding. Masson and his fellow passengers expected to be killed and fed to the sharks, but to their relief the pirates put them on a German vessel bound for Baltimore, where they were transferred to another boat heading for New York. It was a wretched voyage, made worse by the vile weather. They were treated as third-class citizens, being allowed to sleep only on the cables, and fed on a diet of half a pound of black bread made from the husks of wheat and rye, and three and a half pints of bad water a day.

Eventually they docked in New York and Masson made his

way to Canada, where he set about collecting with his customary energy. According to the Kew Inwards Book he sent home the seeds of three species of prunus, two esclepias, a trillium, a trifolium and a viola, as well as a spiraea, a kalmia and two roses. Altogether he gathered twenty-four new species, but this was nothing compared to his great South African collections.

The hard climate did not suit Masson, after his years in the sun of Africa and the tropics. He became unwell and, after a short illness, died in Montreal on 23 December 1805, at the age of sixty-six, a lonely death far from home and friends. He was buried on Christmas Day.

His contribution to gardens and botany was enormous. Nearly half of all known pelargoniums were introduced by him, and of the 786 plates in the first twenty volumes of Curtis's Botanical Magazine, almost a third are devoted to Cape plants, the majority of which were collected for Kew by Masson. His skilful drawings and watercolours of South African plants are now in the British Museum. The weird stapelias, or carrion flowers, the popular greenhouse ericas, scores of bulbous plants, and many annuals which are now familiar bedding plants can all be credited to Britain's first official plant collector. Even though they are familiar today, it is not hard to imagine the sensation caused by such discoveries as *Zantedeschia aethiopica* (the arum lily), *Amaryllis belladonna* (the pale-pink belladonna lily) and *Strelitzia reginae* (the bird of paradise flower), which headed the list of exotic plants sent from Kew in 1795 as a gift to the Empress Catherine of Russia.

Writing to Sir Edward Smith after Masson's death, James Lee the younger, son of the famous Hammersmith nurseryman, said of the 'Scots garden hand' that:

> He has done so much for botany and science, and deserves to have some lasting memorial given to his extreme modesty, good temper, generosity and usefulness.

That memorial blooms every year throughout the world, in private gardens and public parks, where the descendants of his wonderful introductions remain enduring favourites.

ALLAN CUNNINGHAM
(1791-1839)

Joseph Banks had never forgotten the marvellous plants, shrubs and trees he saw flowering in the apparently hostile Australian landscape, and when he became unofficial Director of the Royal Botanic Gardens at Kew he longed to see a comprehensive collection of the plants growing and flourishing in the hot-houses there. The first gardeners he sent to New South Wales to collect for Kew, eighteen years after his return in 1771, were George Austin and James Smith, who seemed to have found few new plants. They were followed twenty-one years later by George Caley, who distinguished himself more for making trouble than plant hunting, although he did send quantities of seed back to Sir Joseph. The botanist Robert Brown, who became librarian to Sir Joseph, also added to the growing flow of plants and seeds from the other side of the world; and it was through Banks, too, that perhaps the greatest of all the collectors of Australian plants, Allan Cunningham, was sent to the raw young country.

Allan Cunningham was born on 13 July 1791, in Wimbledon, now a populous London suburb but then a country area. His brother, Richard, was born fifteen months later and both were educated in Putney. Their father was a Scotsman from Renfrewshire, and their mother was from Shropshire. The Cunningham family life seems to have been fairly uneventful, and on leaving school Allan worked in a conveyancer's office in Lincoln's Inn. It was a life he found utterly tedious, so he left to become clerk at Kew to William Townsend Aiton, the Royal Gardener, and he assisted in the production of the second edition of the Kew catalogue, *Hortus Kewensis*. It was through this work that he met Robert Brown, came to the notice of Sir Joseph Banks, and was selected to collect for Kew in Australia.

With James Bowie, a gardener at Kew, Cunningham sailed from Plymouth in HMS *Duncan* on 29 October 1814. On Christmas Day they reached Rio de Janeiro, where the two men based themselves to spend three months collecting in the vicinity of the city. Then they went to San Paulo, where they stayed from April until August 1815. After another year Bowie was sent to South Africa, and Cunningham continued his journey to New South Wales, arriving on 20 December, 1816 at Sydney Cove, where he was well received by the Governor, Major-General Lachlan Macquarie. After settling at Parramatta, he spent some time finding his feet and botanizing in the surrounding country, collecting *Banksia oblongifolia, Ceratopetalum gummiferum,* and several varieties of *Exocarpus.*

In early 1817 he joined an expedition led by Lt John Oxley, the Surveyor-General, into the country west of the Blue Mountains. The party set out on 3 April, and almost immediately the going was rough. The Nepean river was swollen by floods and they had to swim horses and bullocks across it. The terrain was so bad for the carts that the advance party, of which Cunningham was one, often had to wait for as much as a day for the rest of them to catch up. Water was a constant problem: where it was reasonably plentiful it tended to drain out of peaty soil and be brackish. The area was rich in plants, though, and he collected fine specimens of what he described as 'persoonia, chloranthus and shrubs that seemed very like Boronias', as well as grevilleas and eucalypts.

Heavy rain and bad weather held them up at Bathurst, and on 20 April, heading for Farewell Hill, they plunged into mud so deep that the horses sank in it up to their girths, and the riders had to dismount and lead the animals. Five days later, on the banks of the Lachlan river, whose course they were following, they ran into a band of Aborigines. The men among them were heavily tattooed, wore kangaroo teeth in their ears and cockatoo feathers in their hair. Some of them had their beards divided into three plaits, and they all carried barbed spears, which they had probably been using to catch fish. They seemed friendly, and accepted gifts of meat, and all went well until two of them snatched a pair of muskets and tried to run away. Members of the expedition fired at them as they did so, shooting one of them dead, and the rest of the band made off into the bush. Lightning attacks and sudden changes of mood such as this were to be common features of their encounters with the Aborigines.

Three days afterwards, when they were about to move into completely unknown territory, Cunningham began to carry out a practice which he was to repeat all over the country. This was the sowing of the seeds of fruit, herbs and vegetables. On this occasion he planted peach, quince and oak seeds on the banks of the river. In return he collected a casuarina tree, probably what became known as *Casuarina cunninghamiana*, the she-oak of Australia, and what he called a lotus, which would have been *Nelumbo gigantea* or another of the nelumbo family.

The party, which had grown from ten to thirteen men, and also comprised fourteen horses, dogs and two boats, now took to the water, but soon ran into trouble because fallen trees were blocking the river. The larger of the boats was stove in on a floating tree-trunk, and while it was repaired the party camped by a lagoon full of swans and ducks. Here Cunningham collected a large number of acacia and pittosporum seeds.

By early May the party was back on the water, but split up by a maze of lagoons. They kept in touch by shouting and discharging guns, but were becoming increasingly uneasy because they could hear the voices of Aborigines, but were unable to see them. Eventually, however, they did meet a small group of them, and they found them shy but friendly.

On 8 May they left the river and passed through good country. The dogs brought down an emu, which, with the boiled leaves of a plant Cunningham named *Rhagodia,* provided a feast. But eleven days later they were getting dangerously short of water. By digging holes they were able to find some 'miserable filthy water', and were rationed to one and a half pints each per day. The horses were weakening through thirst, and by 25 May they were in a terrible condition, completely exhausted after struggling through bush so thick and wiry that it pulled the loads from their backs. During the night the wretched animals wandered off in search of food and water, and it took the explorers five days to recover them. Despite these difficulties, Cunningham still had time to botanize, and he found an olearia, an evergreen bush which he described as 'a good blue aster', and a grevillea.

Cunningham then went down with 'a violent ague'; on 1 June one of the horses was so weak it had to be shot; and eight days later they were forced to turn back to where they knew there was good water. They managed to reach it without losing any more animals and, while the horses drank and grazed, the members of the expedition were able to feast on kangaroo-rats (secured by their dogs) and 'excellent good water'. By mid-June they were on the move again, and having to make do with semi-stagnant water from rock holes. The shortage of water became increasingly acute, one of the best pack horses collapsed and died, and the position was worsened by the discovery that a large quantity of flour was missing from the stores. The party had to go on half rations, and even had to eat a dingo which was killed by their dogs.

They reached the Lachlan river and fresh water again on 23 June, but by the beginning of July they were down to a ration of three pounds of flour for each person per week. A week later another horse died, and its flesh was fed to the dogs. They could constantly hear the voices of Aborigines in the bush and felt threatened by the fact that the natives were quite invisible, but even so, when they found an Aborigine grave, Oxley, their leader, decided to open it. He had been instructed to discover all he could about 'the government, customs and habits' of the Aborigines of the country over which they might pass. In it they found the remains of a man six feet tall, and took away the skull.

By 19 August they were travelling through reasonably open, well-watered country, and although there was a dangerous lack of food the situation was eased by the dogs bringing down emus and kangaroos. Cunningham found some good plants, including the shrubby 'potato' or kangaroo apple, *Solanum laciniatum,* with its fine blue flowers and fruits that turn from green to yellow and finally to a rich orange. When they reached Bathurst again, after a round trip of 1200 miles (of which they had actually walked 750) his horse was loaded with kegs stuffed with plants, bulbs and seeds. At the end of August they began the last part of the journey home to Sydney. This was relatively uneventful, except that Cunningham's horse fell in a swamp, which spoiled some of his collections.

On his return to Parramatta on 9 September, after the months on the move, Cunningham found letters from Sir Joseph Banks suggesting he should join a naval expedition which was to explore and thoroughly survey the north and north-west coasts, under the command of Lt Philip Parker King, the son of a former Governor of New South Wales.

The prospect of travelling in a well-run ship was an attractive alternative to slogging through the wilderness, particularly as land travel had not been helped by the stuffy, bureaucratic, obstructive behaviour of Governor Macquarie, who refused to allow the plant hunter to keep the horse he had been loaned for the Oxley expedition. The Governor's reply to his quite reasonable request was, according to Cunningham's journal:

> that it was a sort of indulgence even refused to surveyors and medical officers of the Government, whose various public duties frequently require the use of a horse, and he concluded with observing that were this indulgence extended to me 'they would have reason to complain of so mortifying a distinction'.

Cunningham divined, correctly, that he could expect no help from the Governor or the Government, and he wrote to Sir Joseph that, while he was grateful for his weekly ration of beef and wheat from the Government stores, he had hoped for a small

40

house to use as a base, and a horse. Macquarie got to hear of the letter and its contents and, furious, he summoned Cunningham to tell him that the letter was an attack on him and a personal insult.

While waiting for the expedition to begin, Cunningham filled his time preparing his plants and seeds for shipment to England in the brig *Harriet*. Then, on 21 December, he went aboard the little 84-ton cutter *Mermaid* and sailed with Lt King out of Sydney Cove. At first they were driven back to Port Jackson by foul weather, but five days later they reached Green Cape and anchored in Snug Cove in Twofold Bay. Cunningham went ashore and found a striking pittosporum and *Olearia dentata* (which he referred to as *Aster dentatus*). Wherever conditions seemed suitable, he made small gardens and sowed them from his stock of seeds. He planted peach, apricot and lemon seeds, marrowfat peas, broad beans, scarlet runners, carrots, parsley, celery, parsnips, cabbage, lettuce, endive and spinach, as well as Virginia tobacco, sweet and perpetual peas, and Spanish broom.

From time to time when they went ashore, they came under attack from Aborigines. On the Northern Territory coast they were showered with stones and granite-headed spears, and King ordered a native canoe to be towed away as a reprisal. In St Asaph's Bay they had to beat a hasty and undignified retreat when they were charged by a band of warriors, because they were armed with only one musket. In his journal Cunningham described this approach of the armed men, and recorded:

> A slight confusion instantly took place by the sudden and unexpected alarm, when it was deemed most advisable to make good our retreat to the boat (having but one musket with us), which we accordingly did rather precipitately down the rugged side of the hill we had ascended. Our retreat gave these Australians boldness, and we had scarcely time to secure our instruments in the boat and push off from the shore when seven natives appeared.

The Aborigines hailed the explorers and made signs for them to return to the beach, while at the same time trying to hide their spears. In their hurry and panic the expedition had left on shore some surveying equipment which they now saw being carried away by one of the Aborigines. The natives indicated that they wanted iron axes, and later that day two boats with armed men went ashore and tried unsuccessfully to trade axes for their equipment.

Despite several other brushes with the tribespeople, they managed to survey the Van Diemen Gulf and the coasts of Bathurst and Melville Islands. It was at Bathurst Island that they checked the stores, and found that the rice was unfit to eat, and that while they had enough salt beef and pork for three months, some of the pork casks had leaked and fouled the water supply. There was no alternative but to head for the Dutch colony on the island of Timor to stock up with fresh food, so on 31 May they left the Australian coast and arrived at the port of Kupang and the Dutch Fort, Concordia, on 4 June. While the expedition waited for sheep to be brought down from the mountains, to be added to the stores, Cunningham was able to collect plants on the island.

After ten days they left the island to continue their exploration of the Australian coast. After calling briefly at the tiny Monte Bello Islands on the north-west coast they sailed southwards, and 13 July saw them battling round Cape Leeuwin, the south-western tip of Australia, in the teeth of fierce squalls. Just over eight months after leaving, they dropped anchor once again in Sydney Cove. Cunningham had added impressively to his plant collections, and notable finds included an hibiscus, as well as banksias and grevilleas.

From the end of July to October 1818 he worked from his Parramatta base, and then he spent a month from October to November collecting in the Botany Bay and Liverpool areas. At the beginning of the following year he went to Tasmania with Lt King, and then in May, again with the sailor-explorer, he set out for a further voyage along the Australian coast, this time following the route taken by Cook in the *Endeavour*. Cunningham described this journey in a series of letters to Sir Joseph Banks, who knew the area well.

On 27 May they landed in the estuary of the Endeavour river, probably at the very point where Cook landed his stores in order to lighten the *Endeavour* before he could haul her off the coral. Here King's party had to build a boat, to replace a whaler that had been swamped and lost. 'Thus', Cunningham wrote to Sir Joseph, 'the convenient south shore of the Endeavour River – which probably has never been visited since the departure of Captain Cook in 1770 – has been a second time converted into a temporary dockyard.' History was also repeated when the boat builders were attacked by natives; Cook and his men had had the same trouble. During Cook's stay there the Aborigines had tried to burn the party's tents; Cunningham and his companions also suffered from lightning attacks, made worse by the fact that the warriors moved silently and unseen through the terrain. Their weapons were mostly spears which they threw with great accuracy, adding to their force and range by using a throwing stick, which was a specially shaped piece of wood slotted into the butt of the spear and acting like a sling. The war-parties also carried shields and heavy hardwood clubs for fighting at close quarters, and their boomerangs could break bones and inflict ugly wounds. Nevertheless, botanizing was still possible. In his letter to Banks, Cunningham continued:

> In my various daily walks during the first week of our stay, much pleasure was derived in tracing your steps with those of Dr Solander, and detecting many plants then discovered, that in all probability have never been seen in a living state since that period; among which you may call to remembrance the *Grevillea gibbosa,* in flower and fruit, so prevalent on the rocky hills; the beautiful bluish flowering *Nymphoea* (like the late Dr Roxburgh's *N. versicolor*), expanding itself on the surface of the chains of stagnant pools in the lower lands; and the ornamental *Melastoma banksii* above mentioned, clothing the muddy shaded banks of these small ponds.

Unfortunately his plans to trek inland for two days were frustrated by the very hostile behaviour of the Aborigines, and the fact

43

that Lt King could not spare the men to provide him with an adequate escort. As well as plants, Cunningham found on the beach some coal: it had been left there by Cook fifty years earlier.

Their journey northwards brought them to the Flinders Group of islands in Princess Charlotte Bay, where they found the remains of the *Frederick*, a vessel which had been wrecked on the rocks in 1818 with the loss of twenty-one people. King spent the day cannibalizing the wreck for spare blocks and iron bolts, which their own ship badly needed. In Newcastle Bay the *Mermaid* ran aground on hard sand, and for a time it was feared she would beat herself to pieces. Fortunately she broke free, and in commemoration of this King named the river-like opening which had lured them onto the sandbank 'Escape river'.

On 24 July they rounded Cape York, the northernmost tip of the Australian continent, and hoped to find shelter at Prince of Wales Island, but the vessel dragged her anchor, which broke, and they had to seek refuge on tiny Booby Island. Next, they crossed the Gulf of Carpentaria to the Wessel Islands, and from there made for Goulburn Island to look for water and wood, where they were attacked while digging for water by fusilades of stones, thrown with force and accuracy by the Aborigines. At Port Keats in Joseph Bonaparte Gulf, and also in Cambridge Gulf, Cunningham went ashore and made a number of valuable additions to his acacia collection, which he eventually brought safely back to Sydney.

After the expedition had worked its way west round Cape Londonderry and the Sir Graham Moore Islands, the ship was turned round to head back the way it had come, and by July 1820 they were back at the Endeavour river, where Cunningham dug up a large number of bulbs of what he called *Crinum angustifolium*. He also hunted for plants along the banks of the Roe and Hunter rivers.

Towards the end of the journey it was becoming alarmingly evident that the *Mermaid* was worn out. It was leaking badly, and it was with the greatest difficulty that King managed to steer round Cape Banks, navigating by the light of a terrifying lightning storm. The *Mermaid* was a tiny ship for such major journeys, and its long spells at sea hastened its deterioration. Savage storms and close encounters with rocks, shoals and sandbanks had drastically strained its battered timbers, which anyway had been subjected to attack from marine worms which had eaten into them.

At Sydney the ship was declared unseaworthy, and King was given a 165-ton teak-built brig, the *Haldane,* which was now renamed the *Bathurst.* Cunningham was aboard for the maiden voyage of exploration, which left Sydney on 26 May 1821. They reached South Goulburn Island on 5 July, and from there sailed west to the Prince Regent river, where they had their most serious clash with the natives. During the fighting the ship's surgeon, Mr Montgomery, was struck in the back by a spear, which caused a painful but not fatal wound. In the battle that followed, an Aborigine was wounded by a musket ball and, to punish the natives further, their canoes, weapons, fishing lines and water baskets were seized.

From here they voyaged west to the Buccaneer Archipelago, named to commemorate the pirate William Dampier, who had made the first accurate observations of the country sixty years before Banks. Here the *Bathurst* was drawn into a narrow strait by the tide and nearly wrecked on the rocks. The vessel was damaged, and so King decided to sail to Mauritius in the Indian Ocean, for repairs and to buy anchors and cables. They arrived on 26 September, and Cunningham busied himself botanizing in the hills and studying the plants in the Botanic Gardens.

Back in Australian waters and heading for home, they found themselves again in trouble at Cape Lévêque, where a strong, racing tide swept them through a cluster of small islands. One strait was no more than a hundred yards wide, and at one stage their rudder was only six feet from the jagged rocks, but fortunately they passed through these dangerous waters without further damage to their ship.

This was the last voyage that Cunningham made with King. After their return to Sydney, he settled down for a time at Parramatta, making occasional forays into the bush locally and around Bathurst (on one trip losing his pack horses), and then he made another trip across the Blue Mountains, and also accompanied Oxley on his second survey of the Brisbane River in Queensland. For the greater part of 1826 he was in New Zealand, and returned to New South Wales with a fine collection of flora from the islands in January 1827. Soon after this he led an expedition to locate the Darling Downs in Queensland, an arduous journey through dense bush which had to be hacked away with axes. However, the first view of the Downs – which were open, grassy and well watered – showed that the months-long trip had been worth while.

By 1828 Cunningham was growing homesick, and made it clear that he wanted to return to England. Even so, the following year he was still exploring new territory, on a trip to Queensland, returning to Sydney with seventy boxes of plants he planned to carry triumphantly home to Kew. It was not until November 1830 that he received his recall, and on 10 July 1831 he arrived in England. He set up home in a house at Strand-on-the-Green on the banks of the Thames, only a few minutes walk from Kew, and there he worked on his huge collections.

Whether because of the cold, grey, damp weather of Britain, or the indestructible memory of a vast country, bright and vivid under an endless blue sky, Cunningham could not settle down, and in 1837 he returned to New South Wales to take up the post of Colonial Botanist, even though four years earlier his brother Richard, who had sailed to Port Jackson in Australia, had been murdered by Aborigines. He soon tired of Government work, however, and decided to become a freelance collector. He made a second trip to New Zealand, where he fell ill, and he was still a sick man when he returned to Sydney. He died in June 1839.

In his last letter to Robert Brown, he had written, 'I am now exhausted in subject and literally in body, I therefore close, begging you, my dear sir, to receive this letter from the hands of a poor, decrepit, prematurely old traveller.' Allan Cunningham had worn himself out with tireless travelling, opening up a new land and collecting the marvellous flora he loved.

DAVID DOUGLAS
(1799-1834)

David Douglas had always been a creature of the wild. Born in Scone in Perthshire, he was the despair of his stonemason father and his teachers; when he should have been at his lessons he was invariably out truanting in the hills around his home. He was fascinated by the natural world about him, and would catch and tame wild animals, buying food for them with the money given to him for his midday meal.

At the age of ten he was made an apprentice gardener to the Earl of Mansfield, and displayed such an intelligent and enquiring interest in plants that the Earl let him use the fine collection of botanical books in his library. When he was twenty-one Douglas joined the staff of the Royal Botanic Gardens in Glasgow, and three years later was chosen by the Horticultural Society, now the Royal Horticultural Society, in London, to collect for it in North America.

On Saturday, 9 April 1825, after a voyage of eight months and two weeks, Douglas set foot in North America at Cape Disappointment. A thick, cold fog shrouded the coast, dispersed only by teeming rain, but he was no sooner ashore than he began plant hunting. The first plant he found for his collection was the evergreen shrub *Gaultheria shallon,* with its racemes of pink and white flowers and dark purple berries. The countryside was rich with fine timber trees, including *Pseudotsuga menziesii,* the aromatic Douglas fir, which he introduced into cultivation in Britain in 1827.

He made his base at Fort Vancouver, where he was allocated a small tent, but his rapidly growing collections soon made this inadequate and he moved into an Indian wigwam made of deer skins. Outgrowing this too, he was finally given a hut built from the bark of the western red cedar (*Thuya plicata*), but during winter the hut would frequently flood with over a foot of water.

With little comfort or luxury at the fort, even the simplest pleasure took on a special delight. In his journal he wrote of the sheer enjoyment of eating freshly caught salmon which had been 'cooked under the shade of a lordly pine on rocky dell far removed from the abodes of civilized life'. Despite the fact that the region was populated by large numbers of Indians who were clearly hostile, it was, he said, possible to anticipate a night sleeping on a bed of branches with the greatest pleasure:

> The luxury of a night's sleep on a bed of pine branches can only be appreciated by those who have experienced a route over a barren plain, scorched by the sun, or fatigued by groping their way through a thick forest, crossing gullies, dead wood, lakes, stones, etc.

There were times when he was so exhausted at the end of a day in the field that he would crawl on hands and knees into camp. Once he put some partridges on his fire to boil and fell asleep, waking to find his supper burned to a cinder and his kettle destroyed. The following morning he had to brew his tea in the lid of his tinder box. Food was a constant problem, and when game or fish were not available the alternative was often starvation, and travellers could not depend on the pioneers who had settled in the wilderness to help them.

In 1826, the year before he returned to England, he was collecting in Spokane in the State of Washington, where he found the settlers starving. Spokane was almost a ghost town, but at the end of an arduous journey he was glad to reach it. The most hazardous part of the journey had been crossing the

Barrière river; it was May, and melting snow and ice had swollen the river into a raging torrent. The horses had to be unharnessed so that they could swim across, leaving Douglas to bring his essential baggage over as best he could. Twice he crossed and recrossed the flood, stripped naked and swimming on his back so he could hold equipment and collections up above the bitterly cold water. Half-way through this painful operation he was lashed by a hail-storm. But he was still able to spot a new and highly variable phlox, which produced blue, pink and white flowers.

That night he lodged with Jacques Raphael Finlay and his family, who were reduced to eating roots and a kind of leathery pancake made out of lichen collected from the pine trees. For once Douglas had a good stock of food with him which he shared with them. However, despite the lack of food in the Finlay household, their settlement was infested with a species of rat. Douglas described this 'curious rat' in a letter dated July 1826 to Joseph Sabine, Secretary of the Horticultural Society, as being ten inches long, with a seven-inch tail, a light brown back and a near-white belly. The rats must have been desperate for food, for in the night they swarmed into his tent, ate his seed collections and gnawed through a bundle of dried plants. They had also already carried off his razor and shaving brush, and were in the process of dragging his inkstand out of the tent, when he woke up. He always kept his gun, loaded, by his side at night, and with a shot he managed to save his inkstand, but little else.

At the beginning of that year, Douglas had been in low spirits. Writing in his journal on 1 January at Fort Vancouver, he reflected gloomily that in 1824 he had sailed from England filled with the highest hopes for the future. In 1825 he had been deep in the Pacific between Juan Fernandez and the Galapagos, and 'I am now here, and God only knows where I may be next. In all probability, if a change does not take place, I will shortly be consigned to the tomb. I can die satisfied with myself. I never have given cause for remonstrance or pain to an individual on earth. I'm in my twenty-seventh year.'

49

In fact, of all his years in North America, 1826 proved to be the most spectacularly successful. He travelled nearly 4000 miles by canoe, horse and on foot, collecting a large number of plants and seeds, and made an historic climb in the Blue Mountains in Oregon. He began his travels of 1826 on the Columbia river, leaving Fort Vancouver on 20 March. The journey through the Grand Rapids was magnificent: massive conifers grew on the mountainsides that sloped down to the river; the snow contrasted brilliantly with the dark green of the trees; and radiant rainbows were formed by the spray thrown up by the river as it roared and boomed through the valleys.

While Douglas and his companions marvelled at the country through which they were travelling, the Indians who inhabited it viewed them with suspicion and hostility. As more and more Europeans arrived, it must have been evident to the tribes that they were gradually losing their traditional hunting grounds to the invaders. But while they mistrusted the white people, they were at the same time fascinated by their apparently magical powers. For example, Douglas regularly dosed himself with an effervescent drink which he took for his health, and when the Indians saw him drink the mixture they thought he was drinking boiling water, a feat that could only possibly be achieved by a bad spirit. He also astounded them by lighting his pipe using a magnifying glass and the rays of the sun; but it was his spectacles that had the most devastating effect. He only had to put them on for every Indian to cover his mouth with his hands in a gesture of dread. Generally, however, he got on well with the tribes, who called him the 'Grass Man' because of his habit of collecting plants, which seemed eccentric to the Indians. His particular friend was Cockqua, a kind of high king of both the Chinook and Chochali tribes, who was 'exceedingly fond of all the chiefs that come from King George', and always gave Douglas a warm welcome. Typical of his hospitality was an occasion when, following the formal greetings, Douglas was led by the chief to a canoe in which he had a ten-foot-long sturgeon, and asked to choose which part he would like from the fish. Douglas recorded:

I gave him the preference as to knowledge about the
savoury mouthfuls, which he took as a great compliment.
In justice to my Indian friend, I cannot but say he afforded
me the most comfortable meal I had had for a considerable time before, from the spine and head of the fish.

Cockqua at the time was at war with the Cladsap tribe, camped
on the opposite bank of the river. He urged Douglas to sleep
close to him for safety, but the explorer knew that if he did so he
would be judged a coward and lose face with the tribe. He
therefore pitched his tent some fifty yards from the village, and
spent a restless night listening to a war dance and the singing of
death songs. The following morning he was greeted as a hero for
having braved the Cladsap threats.

This praise for the white man obviously annoyed one of
Cockqua's young braves, who strutted up to Douglas and
proceeded to demonstrate his skill as a warrior. With his bow
he shot arrows through small grass hoops that were thrown
high into the air, and with a rifle put a ball within an inch of a
mark three hundred yards away. No chief from King George,
he boasted, could match his shooting, or sing a death song or
dance a war dance. Douglas had to answer the challenge and,
knowing that the Indians knew nothing of shooting birds on the
wing, loaded his gun with swan-shot and walked towards an
eagle which was perched on a stump close to the village. When
he was about fifty feet from the bird he tossed a stone at it,
and as it rose into the air he shot it. The Indians were deeply
impressed, except for his challenger, who threw his hat into the
air and told Douglas to shoot it. He did so, blasting away the
crown and leaving only the brim. In this way he found that he
could often gain a useful psychological advantage if he casually
shot a bird on the wing as he approached a strange Indian village.

Not all Douglas's encounters with the Indians were as
pleasant as those with Cockqua and his people. On the Columbia
river in the same year, Douglas and the party he was travelling
with found themselves surrounded by more than four hundred
aggressive Indians intent on robbing their canoes. They refused
peace offerings of tobacco, and began throwing water over the

locks of the guns to render them useless, at the same time preventing the travellers from launching their boats. A Mr McLeod in the party gave one Indian a shove, and in response the man immediately notched an arrow in his bow and pointed it at him. Douglas wrote:

> As I was standing on the outside of the crowd I perceived it, and, as no time was to be lost, I instantly slipped the cover off my gun, which at the time was charged with buckshot, and presented it at him, and invited him to fire his arrow, and then I should certainly shoot him.

The war of nerves seemed to last an eternity, but in the end bloodshed was averted by the intervention of the chief of the Kyeuuse, a magnificent man who stood almost six and a half feet tall, and three braves. The chief was a particular friend of Douglas, the first to nickname him the 'Grass Man'.

Sometimes disagreements with the Indians did end in blows. Once, Douglas had his knife stolen, and offered a reward of tobacco if it was returned, but when this achieved nothing, he seached the Indians with him. He eventually found the knife on one of them, who calmly demanded the tobacco before he would return it. 'I paid him, and paid him well with my fists that he will, I dare say, not forget the man of grass for some days to come', he recorded in his journal.

In June he was in the Blue Mountains of Oregon. For any explorer, the supreme experience must be to be the first stranger, perhaps the first person ever, to set foot on unmapped territory. At once the discomfort and exhaustion, the pain and the danger must surely fade away in the sheer triumph of the moment. Douglas often enjoyed the experience but perhaps never so dramatically as when he climbed to the highest point of the Blue Mountains.

With an Indian guide he rode to within 1500 feet of the summit of the range. Here the snow became so deep and soft it was impossible for the horses to continue and so, taking only a gun and some paper for preserving plants, he set off alone on foot. Having no snow-shoes, he was floundering waist-deep in the drifts for the first thousand feet of the final ascent, but within a few hundred feet of the highest peak the surface of the snow had frozen to a hard crust and his progress was swift. Later, he recorded in his journal, 'I without the least difficulty placed my foot on the highest peak of those untrodden regions where never European was before me'.

His clothes, soaked through from wading in soft snow, stiffened and froze in the bitter cold, but he was hardly aware of the discomfort. All around, as far as he could see, was spread a magnificent wilderness of mountains, snow, ice and forest. For three-quarters of an hour he stood mesmerized, and then, suddenly and unexpectedly, the scene changed; huge black clouds enveloped the peaks and with them came a storm of dreadful violence. Thunder and lightning, hail and wind roared, crackled and howled around him. In his journal he declared:

> I never beheld anything that could equal the lightning. Sometimes it would appear in massive sheets, as if the heavens were in a blaze; at other, in vivid zig-zag flashes at short intervals with the thunder resounding through the valleys below, and before the echo of the former peal died away the succeeding was begun, so that it was impressed on my mind as if only one.'

The stunted pines on the mountainside were no protection against the cutting hail driven by the vicious wind. Half blinded by the hail, Douglas staggered into his camp just as darkness was falling. He had not eaten since breakfast, and then had had only a little dried salmon and water from a spring, but it was impossible to light a fire and he had to make do with the same again. Wretchedly cold, he stripped off his wet clothes, wrapped himself in a blanket and slept, but at midnight he woke, 'so benumbed with cold that on endeavouring to get up I found my knees refused to do their office'. He rubbed some life into his legs, and since the storm had spent itself, managed to light a fire and brew a can of tea.

Douglas seemed to be largely impervious to hunger, and would frequently set off for a gruelling day's collecting with only a few biscuits and a pinch of tea in his pack. Usually he managed to live off the land (although on his return to the coast from the Blue Mountains he did have to kill a horse to feed to the Indians in his small party). For this man, plant collecting was the only purpose in life and, despite storm and tempest in the Blue Mountains, he came away with a fine harvest of seeds that included those of *Paeonia brownii* and the fine golden tree lupin, *Lupinus arboreus*.

Many explorers in the past, particularly naturalist-explorers spending long periods alone in isolation, have suffered bouts of melancholia. Hardship, the frustration of bad weather, and a sense of having been forgotten by those at home, all this could produce a depression bordering on despair; but often it required no more than the arrival of mail or a meeting with a fellow countryman to convert gloom into exuberance. Travelling through the wilderness some days after his climb in the Blue Mountains, Douglas spotted smoke rising in the distance. He took it to mark an Indian fishing camp, and hurried towards it to buy fresh supplies, but to his delight he found it to be the camp of a group of European settlers. He wrote excitedly in his journal:

> I cannot describe the feeling that seizes me even on seeing a person again, although I am but partially acquainted with them. After travelling in the society of savages for days together and can but speak words of their language, assuredly the face of a Christian although strange speaks friendship.

Not only were they friends, but they had with them a bundle of mail for Douglas. They fussed round him, bringing him hot water for a wash, a clean shirt, and a cooked meal, but all this was nothing compared to the letters. Four times during that night he got up, lit a lamp and read them, until in the morning he virtually had them off by heart. 'There is a sensation felt on receiving news after such a long silence, and in such a remote corner of the globe, more easily felt than described', he wrote. On another occasion, when he was told by travellers that there was mail waiting for him on the coast, he was cast into great gloom because he could not lay his hands on the letters there and then.

Douglas was not a man to be down for long, however, and the excitement and satisfaction of exploration and the discovery of new plants easily raised his spirits. During a trip on which he had discovered the lovely *Fritillaria pudica*, the only American fritillary, and the great western yellow pine, *Pinus ponderosa,* he came close enough to the Rocky Mountains to know that he should go there and search them for plants. He wrote home to declare, 'I cannot in justice to the Society's interest do otherwise', and did some plant hunting in their foothills.

At the end of July 1826 Douglas was again facing problems with the Indians. He and his party had returned from a particularly wearying journey, and all were deeply asleep when the entire camp was woken by a furious row that had broken out between his interpreter and a local chief. There was a scuffle and the interpreter had a handful of hair torn from his scalp. The chief, who was roundly abused by Douglas and the other Europeans in the camp, stormed off in a rage and returned with a war party of seventy-three men armed with guns and bows. Asked if they wanted to do battle, they said no, they only wanted the interpreter so that they could kill him. After all, they argued, he was not a chief, so his death would be of little consequence. Douglas and his companions naturally refused to hand over the man to face what would have undoubtedly been a horrible end, and it was only after a great deal of speech-making that the tension eased and the dispute ended, with an exchange of presents instead of shots and blows.

Similar problems arose yet again at Kettle Falls on the Columbia river. Here Douglas again had to use all his powers of oratory and diplomacy to bring about peace, when a quarrel broke out and resulted in two parties of naked, painted Indians marching on one another.

Bizarre though the Indians may have appeared to him, Douglas must also have cut a strange figure to them. Because he was so wretchedly paid by the Horticultural Society he was dressed in rags most of the time. When he made a return trip to the Blue Mountains in August 1826 his wardrobe consisted of a shirt, a pair of stockings, a night cap and a pair of old mittens. A gift of a pair of deerskin trousers came just in time, as his own were falling to pieces, but when he returned to Fort Vancouver he was down to the trousers, shirt and an old straw hat; his shoes and stockings had disintegrated.

Undeterred, he set off less than a month later in search of the sugar pine (*Pinus lambertiana*), the largest of all the pines. On his way he gathered a good harvest of ripe seed from plants including *Penstemon richardsonii*, with its snapdragon-like flowers, the hardy flowering shrub *Spiraea tomentosa*, which grew in thickets, and *Pinus resinosa*, the red pine, a fine, tall-growing tree.

Towards the end of October, as he was approaching the territory of the sugar pine, he was caught in a storm which dwarfed all the others he had endured. 'Last night was one of the most dreadful I ever witnessed', he wrote in his journal. The rain was so heavy that it put out his fire, and his tent was blown down. The only cover he could get was to wrap himself in a blanket and then in the tent. Sleepless, he lay in the sodden bracken listening to the thunder and the roaring wind, and hearing the crash of huge trees being toppled by the storm, as the whole demented scene was illuminated by flashes of lightning. 'My poor horses were unable to endure the violence of the storm without craving my protection, which they did by hanging their heads over me and neighing', he wrote. The storm died with the dawn, and Douglas had to make a fire and strip off his wet clothes before trying to rub some life back into his frozen body with a handkerchief.

His night of misery was rewarded the following day with his first sight of a sugar pine. It was a triumphant moment, actually to stand beneath the towering trees which matched even the most extravagant descriptions he had received of them. Their trunks were remarkably straight and smooth-barked, and they were not only beautiful but also immense: one fallen tree he measured was 215 feet long; a yard from the ground it had a girth of more than fifty-seven feet. Although the tree got its name from the sap which was used as a sugar substitute, the cones also bore a likeness to the sugar loaves then sold in grocery shops.

As usual, his moment of triumph was attended by danger. One problem with the sugar pine from Douglas's point of view was the lack of lower branches, which meant that the only way he could collect seed from the upper branches was by shooting the cones off them. He was busily potting away at the cones when a party of eight Indians appeared on the scene, all painted with red earth and heavily armed with bows and arrows, flint knives and bone-headed spears. It was evident that they were anything but friendly. When Douglas explained to them what he was doing, they seemed satisfied and sat down to smoke. Smoking was normally a sign of peace but, as Douglas later recounted, it evidently was not in this case, for one of the Indians slowly and deliberately strung his bow, while another worked up the edge of his flint knife with a wooden strop shaped like a pair of pincers. Douglas could not escape by running away, but he was determined to fight for his life, so without warning he stepped back, cocked his gun and drew a pistol from his belt. The minutes passed with agonizing slowness while the Scot and the Indians eyed one another in silence. After about eight minutes one of the Indians, evidently the leader, made a sign for tobacco, and Douglas agreed to give them some if they first went and collected cones for him.

As silently as they had come, they filed off among the trees and as soon as they were out of sight Douglas picked up his cones and ran back towards his camp. He spent a wretched night lying in the long grass with his gun beside him, expecting an attack at any moment. To pass the time he wrote up his journal by the light of a Columbian candle, which was a piece of resin-rich wood. As dawn came and the dark shadows of the woods faded, he could see that nothing moved among the rocks and the tall, straight trunks of the conifers, and could ascertain that there were no Indians. He was able to pack up his meagre camp and retreat from the land of the sugar pine. Fortunately the cones he collected were large and packed with ripe seed which reached England in good condition.

By the end of 1826 Douglas could look back on a thoroughly satisfactory year. He had assembled a large collection of plants, and had quantities of good seed packed in a tin trunk. He now decided to accompany the group of men and boats known as the Hudson Bay Express from Fort Vancouver to York Factory on the Bay, where he would be able to pick up a boat for home. It was a tough journey which would take him across the Rockies to Lake Winnipeg and the Grand Rapids to Hudson Bay.

On 20 March 1827 the Express set out, and in under a month was within the shadow of the Rockies. He wrote, 'As far as the eye can behold nothing is to be seen but huge mountains, ridge towering above ridge in awful grandeur, their summits wrapped in eternal snow, destitute of timber, and no doubt affording but scant verdure of any sort'. In that latter observation he was wrong. Many fine alpines have been discovered in the heights of the Rockies, but he could be forgiven for being overwhelmed by the sheer size and awesomeness of the range through which he was travelling.

Towards the end of April they left the Columbia river and struck off across country through particularly unpleasant terrain – swampland covered by a thin coating of ice which broke under their weight, plunging them up to their knees in freezing mud and water; and when they climbed up into hilly country they had to contend with snowdrifts up to seven feet deep.

Douglas found the going difficult, largely because he never really mastered the art of walking in snow-shoes; either he became entangled in the brushwood or tripped over his own feet. Nevertheless, he did manage to climb a mountain about 5500 feet above sea-level. From the peak of this mountain he was confronted by a magical scene. Range after range of mountains reached as far as he could see; snow sparkled and glittered; and glaciers were of an azure colour, with rainbow lights glancing off the broken ice. Icicles like pillars reached down from the rocks, and the great silence was broken only by the dull roar of avalanches which threw up snow particles that hung in the air like smoke. Here he put his snow-shoes to good use: he lashed them together and used them as a toboggan for the descent – 'sometimes I came down at one spell five hundred to seven hundred feet in the space of one minute and a half'.

The Hudson Bay Express lived up to its name by setting an exhausting pace; in one day Douglas marched forty-three miles on an empty stomach. With exhaustion there was also danger, as when one of the party, a Mr Finan McDonald, was chased and gored by a bull during a buffalo hunt for fresh provisions. In the hope that the animal might charge past him, McDonald threw himself on the ground, but the animal tossed him into the air, cutting open his right thigh to the bone. Five times more he was struck by the sharp curved horn, and as the bull came in for a seventh blow, McDonald grabbed hold of the long, matted hair on its head and hung on, and they both fell to the ground, the man beneath the animal. Before anyone from the camp could intervene, a gun was accidentally fired. The shot roused the bull, and it stood up, gently turned over the unconscious man and walked away.

Amazingly, the gored man was still alive. The heaviest blow had been to his left side, but much of its force had been absorbed by a double sealskin pouch containing ball, shot and wadding, which covered his heart. Although the horn had passed through the pouch, a coat, vest and two shirts, it had only bruised the skin and broken two ribs. His body was a mass of bruises, there was a deep cut on his right thigh, and his left wrist was dislocated. Douglas dressed his wounds, bled him and gave him a strong dose of laudanum before he was rushed to the settlement of Carlton where there was a doctor, and where he made a complete recovery.

Five months after setting out from Fort Vancouver, Douglas arrived at York Factory, where he was to take passage in the homeward-bound *Prince of Wales*. With two companions he paid a courtesy call on the vessel, anchored in the bay, but on the journey back to shore their small boat was blown seventy miles out to sea by a violent wind-storm. It was only by the greatest good fortune that they were able to regain land.

A little over three years after setting out for North America, Douglas arrived home in Britain. He was immediately lionized, and awarded honorary membership of such learned societies as the Geological Society, the Linnean Society and the Zoological Society. This public recognition appears to have gone to his head, however: he became arrogant and quarrelled with a number of people, including the Horticultural Society Secretary, Sabine, and it was only the intervention of the great botanist and then Director of Kew, Sir William Hooker, that saved his career from ruin.

However unpleasant his behaviour, gardeners owe him a great debt. The 1824-7 expedition yielded a wealth of new plants which have become firm garden favourites, and in some cases, like that of the yellow monkey-flower, *Mimulus moschatus*, naturalized. Douglas brought home *Lupinus polyphyllus*, a parent of the famous Russell lupins; the popular ornamental currant, *Ribes;* the Oregon grape, *Mahonia aquifolium;* and the lovely dogwood, *Cornus alba.*

In 1829 he returned to America, and during the following three years extended his hunting-grounds down the Pacific Coast to California. Although he did not introduce it to Europe, he did visit and describe the giant redwood (*Sequoia gigantea*) and he collected such splendid annuals as the Californian poppy (*Eschscholzia californica*), *Clarkia elegans* which has given rise to brilliantly coloured hybrids, the godetias, and *Limnanthes douglasii,* the poached-egg plant, beloved by both bees and gardeners. Undoubtedly one of the finest plants he collected was *Garrya elliptica,* which produces glorious trusses of catkins in late winter, when gardens are at their barest.

Sadly, little is known of Douglas's last expedition because his journals were destroyed in an accident. Certainly he had planned to return home through Alaska and Siberia, but in the end he chose to make his way to Hawaii, drawn by a fascination for volcanoes, which he wanted to study at close quarters. He decided to explore the interior of the island, and climb to the three active volcanoes, Mauna Loa, Mauna Kea and Kilauea.

On the morning of 12 July 1834, with his dog Billy, his

inseparable companion, he stopped to have breakfast at the hut of an ex-Botany Bay convict, Ned Gurney, who lived in the mountains of Hawaii. Gurney made his living from trapping the wild cattle which roamed the slopes. His method was crude but effective: he dug deep pits, covered them with a flimsy camouflage, and waited for the animals to fall in. Then he would kill them with a single shot. When Douglas left him, Gurney warned him to watch out for the pits; but this was to be the last time he was seen alive.

Later that day his dog was found guarding Douglas's backpack. Close by was a cattle-pit containing a wild bullock, and the mangled body of the plant hunter. The cruel irony was that ever since witnessing the goring of McDonald, Douglas had nursed a morbid dread of cattle. His bizarre and horrible death inspired many rumours and theories. Some said he had been murdered following a quarrel, others that Gurney had pushed him into the pit because he thought he was having an affair with his wife. It was even claimed that he had committed suicide.

There is no evidence to support these fanciful notions. It is much more likely that Douglas's insatiable curiosity drew him to the pit and that he either overbalanced or the side gave way under his weight. Whatever happened, it seems particularly tragic that a man who brought so much beauty to gardens all over the world should die such an ugly death.

ROBERT FORTUNE
(1813-80)

In the nineteenth century China held Europe in the grip of wonder and avarice: legend and travellers' tales had invested it with a special mystery and magic, and it seemed an endless source of almost unimaginable riches. All European countries of substance nursed the ambition to gain a foothold in China, to win its wealth through trade or, perhaps, through conquest. It was hardly surprising, therefore, that while the Europeans eyed the country greedily, the Chinese regarded the acquisitive strangers with suspicion and distrust.

During the latter part of the eighteenth century, throughout the nineteenth and into the twentieth, China was an apparently inexhaustible source of fine plants, most of which thrived in British gardens. During the eighteenth century a number of fine introductions were made, but because the native gardeners and nurserymen were so secretive about their plants and extremely reluctant to part with so much as a seed or a cutting to foreigners, it was assumed, correctly, that there was much of beauty and value yet to be discovered. Even so, when the still-young Horticultural Society of London decided to send Robert Fortune to China in 1843, its Council could not have guessed at the huge number of horticultural treasures that waited to be discovered in the mountains and wild places of the vast country. The Society was content that Fortune should, in the nicest possible way, plunder the nursery gardens that protected their plants behind high walls and locked gates.

Robert Fortune was born at Edrom, Berwickshire, in Scotland, and educated at the local parish school. Coming from a humble home, he was unable to take his schooling further than the elementary stage, and was apprenticed to a local nurseryman. Eventually he took up a post at the Royal Botanic Gardens in Edinburgh, and from there he moved to London to take charge of the indoor plant section of the Horticultural Society gardens, then at Chiswick. He so impressed the Society with his ability both as a gardener and a botanist that its Council decided he should be their man in China. Their choice was a sound one. Fortune was extremely industrious, as well as cool-headed, and unlikely to come to harm or do anything foolhardy in a crisis.

The Society's instructions to Fortune, dated 23 February 1843, were clear and formidable:

> You will embark on board the *Emu* in which a berth has been secured for you and where you will mess with the captain.
>
> Your salary will be £100 a year from the time of your quitting charge of the hothouse department until you resume it upon your return from China, clear of all deductions and inclusive of the cost of your outfit or such contingent expenses as may be required in carrying out the objects of the Society.
>
> The general objects of your mission are (1) to collect seeds and plants of an ornamental or useful kind, not already cultivated in Great Britain, and (2) to obtain information upon Chinese gardening and agriculture together with the nature of the climate and its apparent influence on vegetation.

He was given a long list of items to discover, including the peaches of Pekin, grown in the Emperor's garden and said to weigh two pounds apiece; plants yielding tea of different qualities; the conditions under which the shrub *Enkianthus* grew in Hong Kong, and where it could be found in the wild. He was to track down double yellow roses other than *Rosa banksia,* which was already in cultivation; find the plant used to manufacture rice paper; search for blue paeonies, yellow camellias, and the true Mandarin orange. The list also included the lilies of Fukien 'eaten as chestnuts when boiled'; *Oxalis sensitiva;* the azaleas from Ho-fou-shau, a mountain in the Province of Canton; varieties of *Celosia* and *Amaranthus;* varieties of *Illicium;* tree and herbaceous paeonies; varieties of bamboos 'and the uses to which they are applied'. Always he was to look for hardy plants, take soil samples, find out about the art of dwarfing trees, and make herbarium specimens of all he found. Finally, he was instructed, in a rather ungenerous spirit, to sell his firearms before leaving China and return the money to the Society. If he failed to make a sale he was to return the guns.

Fortune arrived off the coast of China on 6 July 1843, four months after sailing from England. The first landfall was at Hong Kong, and from there the ship went up the coast to Amoy which, he recounted later, was the filthiest town he had ever encountered 'either in China or elsewhere; worse even than Shanghai and that is bad enough'. Indeed, Fortune quickly realized that the travellers' tales he had heard were grossly exaggerated. He wrote in his account of his three years in the country:

> There can be no doubt that the Chinese Empire arrived at its highest state of perfection many years ago; and since then it has rather been retrograding than advancing. Many of the northern cities, evidently once in the most flourishing condition, are now in a state of decay, or in ruins; the pagodas that crown the distant hills, are crumbling to pieces and apparently are seldom repaired.

Although he found the people of this southern coastal town difficult and dangerous, 'being remarkable for their hatred to foreigners and conceited notions of their own importance, besides abounding in characters of the very worst description, who are nothing less than thieves and pirates', generally he liked and admired the Chinese. He got to know them intimately during his treks in the hills, and from sleeping in their temples and

John Tradescant Senior (above) was not only a
superb gardener but also the father of modern
plant hunting. In his pursuit of new trees and
flowers for royalty and the nobility he took on the
roles of soldier, sailor and emissary. He was also a
tireless collector of curiosities of natural and
human design, and his remarkable 'Cabinet of
Curiosities' at his Lambeth home in London
formed the basis of the celebrated Ashmolean
Museum in Oxford.

The silver birch, *Betula pendula* (above), one of
the most graceful of trees, was found by John
Tradescant in Russia. His son, also John (right,
below), collected in Virginia. Among the many
plants he brought home were the lovely evening
primrose, *Oenothera biennis* (right, above), and one
of the most elegant of lilies, *Lilium canadense* (far
right, above).

S:ʳ John Tradescant Jun.ʳ
in his Garden.

The flamboyant red-hot pokers, kniphofias (left, above), were collected by Francis Masson in South Africa. Allan Cunningham (left, below) suffered great hardship in order to bring the first major harvest of Australian plants to Europe, and David Douglas (below), best remembered for the conifers he discovered in North America, also gathered many fine herbaceous plants such as the poached-egg plant *Limnanthes douglasii* (above).

Many of David Douglas's introductions were so
good that they have been some of the most
popular garden plants ever since. Among them is
the evergreen *Mahonia aquifolium* (top, left and
right), with its fine glossy foliage and dense heads
of fragrant yellow flowers which are followed by
grape-blue berries. Another is the quick-growing
Garrya elliptica (above), whose long pale green
tassels, which appear in the grey days of winter,
seem to bring spring closer.

eating with them in their houses.

It was in Amoy, however, that he had his first taste of the less attractive side of the Chinese character. Wherever he went he found that he was constantly surrounded by people, and he had been warned to keep a sharp eye out for the 'Chinchew' (he probably meant Chuanchou) men, who had a reputation as ruthless robbers and murderers. It was a warning he largely ignored. One day when he and his servant were botanizing in the hills he found himself accompanied by a huge crowd of people, so many that he thought the stones themselves were turning into Chinese. The people seemed friendly until one of them took a fancy to a silk neck-scarf Fortune was wearing. Several of them then tried to trade the scarf for a bottle of spirits. Fortune refused, and the crowd pressed closer. Suddenly he felt a hand in his pocket and, turning round, he saw a man running away with a letter in his hand. It was then he discovered that his pockets had been picked clean.

The mood of the crowd was now ugly, and Fortune looked around for his servant, whom he saw a little way off being attacked by about ten men, who had surrounded him and were threatening him with drawn knives. The bundles of plants he was supposed to guard were flying about in all directions. When they saw Fortune charging up the hill towards them the robbers fled, but nearly all the plants he had collected with such care were trampled and destroyed. However, he did manage to rescue two fine roots of *Campanula grandiflora,* and a new species of abelia (*Abelia rupestris*). Both reached England safely, to flower in the gardens at Chiswick.

The hostility he found in the seaboard towns was partly the creation of European traders and adventurers, but in the north, particularly inland, Fortune noted that 'generally the traveller is not exposed to insult; and the natives are quiet, civil, and obliging'. When he entered a village, the inhabitants would often shout at him to go away, but he found that if he ignored this initial hostility he would quickly be accepted by them. He invariably asked if he could help the large number of sick people. Partial or total blindness was widespread, as were various disfiguring skin diseases, which he put down to dirt and poor diet.

After a short time, Fortune left Amoy by boat, heading first for Ningpo in the Chu-shan Archipelago, and then Shanghai at the mouth of the Yangtze. It was the monsoon season, and his vessel was soon in trouble when it ran into a gale and sprung its bowsprit. Immense waves were whipped up by the howling wind, and the deck was quickly under water. A huge fish, weighing at least thirty pounds, was hurled out of the sea and through the skylight in the poop, landing with a crash on the cabin table in front of the astounded captain. The damage to the ship was so great that, when they did manage to beat their way into harbour, all the cargo, including Fortune's baggage, had to be transferred to another vessel.

Once again they set out, and were nearly through the Formosa Channel (now known as the Formosa Strait – the corridor of sea that separates the mainland from the Nationalist-held island) when another gale bore down on them, ripping the sails to shreds and washing away the bulwarks. The crippled ship was driven back towards the land. Fortune recalled:

> The sea was running very high and awashing our decks fore and aft, as if we had been a narrow plank tossing on the waves. I had gone below, and the captain had come down for a second to look at the barometer, when we felt the sea strike the vessel with a terrible force, and heard a crash which sounded as if her sides had been driven in; at the same time the glass of the skylight came down about our ears, and the sea forced its way into the cabin.

The weather bulwarks had been stoved in and the longboat broken from its moorings and almost carried away. Had it not been held fast by the lee bulwark there is little doubt that it and the crew would have been swept into the sea. As it was, they all escaped with no more than a bad fright and bruises, although two of Fortune's Wardian cases were smashed beyond repair.

Some time later, he found himself again facing danger. He was collecting in the hills outside Canton on the South China Sea, when he was approached by a mounted soldier who, with words and gestures, seemed to be trying to induce him to return to the city. Since Fortune did not understand the Cantonese dialect, and anyway thought the soldier was merely trying to be obstructive, he pressed on. After a few more miles, however, he became uncomfortably aware that he was being watched and followed by small groups of men.

He came to an enclosed area which appeared to be an abandoned cemetery on a hill and, passing through the open door, made for the top of the hill. Before he reached the summit his unwelcome followers crowded round him, demanding presents. Walking quickly to the summit, he looked round and realized he was in a robbers' trap. All he could do was to try to head back to Canton, but hardly had he started down the hill than he was urged to take another route through a ravine, probably so that he could be robbed and stripped and possibly murdered. He refused to follow the men and walked faster, away from them down the hill, but the crowd closed in and held him; his cap was snatched from his head and there were hands in all his pockets. Lashing out blindly, Fortune hurled himself on the people in front of him, sending several of them rolling down the hillside. The impetus of his charge sent him stumbling to the ground, but he recovered himself before he was pinned down. He had to get back through the door in the cemetery wall, otherwise there would be no escape. As he raced down the hill he could hear the men behind him yelling to those in front to close the door. He reached it just as the Chinese on the other side were trying to fasten the locks, threw himself against it and burst it open, flattening the men on the other side.

Out on the road there were some hundreds of Chinese. Many were friendly but too afraid to come to his aid. Stones were flying about his head, and he was brought to the ground by a brick that struck him in the small of his back. For nearly a mile he struggled with his attackers, sometimes fighting, sometimes running, until he was clear of the robbers' territory. His clothes were in rags, he had been robbed of everything of value, and did not even have the price of a cheap coolie hat to keep off the burning sun.

The extremes of weather in China were very uncomfortable for foreigners from temperate climates. During the winter of 1843 in Ningpo, Fortune suffered acutely from the cold, which was worse than anything he had experienced in Britain. In the flimsy house in which he lodged, the icy wind whistled through gaps in the walls and the paper-covered windows, and when he woke in the mornings he would find that snow had blown in during the night and settled on the bedroom floor.

Although Shanghai was then one of the five ports in China where non-Chinese were allowed to trade and set up factories and trading posts, foreigners there were still regarded with the greatest distrust, a mixture of horror and superstition, and were known as the Kwei-tsz, the Devil's Children. For Fortune the problems arising from this attitude were compounded by the fact that the Chinese were very reluctant to part with any plants. Nobody would tell him where he could find nurseries, and the only way he discovered one near Shanghai was by asking some children to take him to the nearest flower garden. When he arrived the gate was slammed in his face and barricaded; but Fortune was a stubborn man, and eventually the nurseryman relented and allowed him to pick out some plants. At the same time he was trying to track down the blue paeony and yellow-flowered species of that genus, but all the blues that Chinese traders brought him turned out to be lilac, purple or nearly black, while the yellows were creamy whites with yellow-tinged stamens. Nevertheless, out of all the paeonies he saw, he was able to assemble a collection of plants that created great excitement when they flowered in England.

While Ningpo and Shanghai did not hold particularly happy associations for him, he loved Chu-shan, a large island off the mouth of the Ningpo river. When he arrived there in 1843 the hillsides were smothered in azaleas in full flower, and he wrote: 'Few can form any idea of the gorgeous and striking beauty of these azalea-clad mountains, where, on every side, as far as our vision extends, the eye rests on masses of flowers of dazzling brightness and surpassing beauty.'

Fortune revelled in the sights and scenes of China, such as

the temple outside Ningpo that stood at the head of a fertile valley, and was approached along a magnificent avenue of Chinese pines, where he collected seeds of the Japanese cedar, *Cryptomeria japonica*. It was here that he first made contact with Buddhist priests, and during his years in China he grew to admire and respect the holy men. He was particularly struck by the way, as vegetarians, they were able to prepare their vegetables in a manner that made the dishes resemble meat. They were kind and considerate. On one occasion when he was being entertained to a meal the priests, monks and their friends sat against the wall smoking and sipping tea. Fortune, a non-smoker, asked them if they would stop while he ate. They did.

The priests protected their food supplies from the wild boars that roamed the region by digging pits as traps, which partially filled with water from the many natural springs. They were carefully camouflaged, and any animal that fell into them drowned. These traps were a considerable source of danger to Fortune as he hunted for plants in the hills, and he had a number of narrow escapes, 'one in particular, when coming out of a dense mass of brushwood, I stepped unawares on the treacherous mouth of one of them, and felt the ground under my feet actually giving way'. Only by grabbing a sapling was he able to save himself from plunging into the deep pit half-filled with water. There would have been little chance of escape, as it was dug in the shape of a huge Chinese vase, wide at the bottom and narrow at the neck; and as he stood looking into the dark water he thought of the dreadful death of David Douglas in a wild bull-pit.

Throughout the summer of 1844, Fortune spent most of his time exploring and collecting on the islands of the Chu-shan Archipelago. Normally it was a pleasant and tranquil experience to travel from island to island in a small boat on the calm, sheltered water, but from time to time sudden and often devastating winds, channelled through the openings in the hills, would sweep over the sea. It was in just such conditions that he nearly lost his life. Fortune was in a hurry to get from Ningpo to Chu-shan, where he wanted to link up with an English vessel lying at anchor in the Bay of Chu-shan. Fearful of missing it before it sailed, he persuaded a local boatman to take him at night, despite a fresh wind and gathering storm clouds. No sooner were they in the open sea than Fortune realized how foolish he had been to insist on making the voyage.

By this time, however, there was no turning back. A strong spring tide and a heavy head wind made it quite impossible for them to return to Chinhai at the mouth of the Ningpo river. Fortune was convinced they were carrying too much sail to survive the strengthening gale, and hardly had the captain assured him that all was well than a tremendous gust struck the boat, at the same time as a freakishly heavy wave. The little craft was laid on its beam end and began to fill with water, and only righted when the sails were lowered; but, being flooded, it rolled so much it seemed they must sink. Eventually they were able to hoist a few feet of sail and thus keep the vessel before the wind. Fortune wrote: 'It was now dark, not a star to be seen in the heavens, the mountains were not distinctly visible, yet loomed through the gloom, and the only objects clearly distinguished were some lights flickering on the distant shore.'

The crew, thoroughly unnerved, tried to persuade the captain to return to Chinhai, but Fortune realized that any attempt to put about would be sure to lead to disaster. He stood by the helmsman to keep off the crew, and ordered the man to hold his course and take the first chance of getting into the lee of an island. Convinced that the mad foreigner was determined to take them to the bottom of the ocean, the panic-stricken crew tore off their clothes, ready to swim for their lives. They refused to work the ship or even bail out the water that had been taken on. Fortunately, a brief lull in the weather made it possible to hoist a little more sail and run for the shelter of a small island. 'As soon as we had anchored all hands began bailing the water out of the boat', recorded Fortune some time later. 'We were in a most pitiable condition, all our clothes and beds being completely soaked with sea water; some plants, but luckily only duplicates, which I had with me were, of course, totally destroyed.'

While the sudden squalls of the Chu-shan Archipelago were frightening enough, for sheer terror there was nothing to match the typhoons which swept land and sea alike. The approach of a typhoon, which the Chinese could sense without the aid of a barometer, was heralded by frantic activity, as fishing fleets ran for the nearest harbour or sheltered creek, along with the larger coasting junks. On land the people attempted to make fast their flimsy houses, and in the fields the farmers and their labourers cut off all the ripe, or nearly ripe, heads of millet; fruit was picked from the trees, whose branches were tied up and supported. The first typhoon that Fortune experienced was at sea, and he was fortunate in being able to run ahead of it into a safe harbour and ride it out at anchor. The second, at Ningpo in 1844, lasted for two days, gradually gaining in force until on 22 August it reached its peak. Fortune described the fearful night that he and a friend, a Mr McKenzie, who were sharing a house, passed together:

> The wind howled and whistled round the roof, every blast seemingly more fierce than that which preceded it, until I really thought we should have the building down upon us and be buried in the ruins. At daylight the rooms presented a dismal appearance; all the floors, chairs and tables were covered with dust, and pieces of broken tiles and mortar which had been shaken off the roof.
>
> As this storm still raged with unabated fury, Mr McKenzie and myself, glad to escape from the wreck by which we were surrounded, went out to see what effect the gale was producing on the other places in the vicinity. The wind was so powerful, that it was next to impossible to keep our feet; in fact, we were frequently blown off the path, and were obliged to scramble back to it again on our hands and knees. The river, which is generally beautiful and smooth, had now risen and completely overflowed its banks, having been forced back by the strength of the wind, and as rough as the sea itself. The whole country is one vast sheet of troubled water, for the branches of the river and the numerous canals by which it is intercepted, had all overflowed their banks, and had spread in the lowly paddy fields.

In one field they came across a family holding down a coffin to prevent it being blown away with the corpse inside it.

Despite storms and typhoons in Ningpo and the Chu-shan Archipelago, Fortune discovered and successfully collected a number of fine plants, including *Azalea ovata, Buddleia lindleyana, Daphne fortuneii,* and *Weigela rosea.*

Land journeys, too, were not without their hazards. The Chinese authorities went to considerable lengths to confine foreigners to the cities and towns, and those that did escape into the open countryside faced an array of pitfalls and problems. Fortune, of course, did get out: in Shanghai he hired a pony and, with the aid of a pocket compass, headed for the hills. At the start all went well. Nobody turned him back, and he negotiated without mishap the innumerable canals which criss-crossed the landscape. When he was within a short distance of the hills he decided to save time by taking a more direct route than that offered by the main highway, but soon he was lost in a maze of tracks and canals. Off the main road the bridges over the canals were dilapidated and dangerous, and again and again his pony's hooves broke through rotten planking. When they came to a bridge even worse than the rest, it collapsed under their weight, and the pony was hurled into the water as Fortune was just able to jump to safety on the shore. Luckily the animal was able to swim back to the bank and, coated in stinking mud, climb ashore to where he was.

Eventually, late that afternoon they reached a small hill town. Failing in his attempts to buy corn for the pony, Fortune allowed himself to be guided by a small boy who led him to an eating house where the animal dined, with obvious relish, on a large bowl of boiled rice.

Part of Fortune's success in being able to move around the country more freely than most foreigners was his ability to pass himself off as a Chinaman. He had acquired a reasonable command of Chinese, and in a country of sharply differing dialects he could always pass as a native from a different province. His first serious experiment with disguise was at Soochow, which he called Soo-Chow-Foo, an inland city not far from Shanghai.

It had a reputation for producing the finest works of art – pictures, carvings, silks – as well as outstandingly beautiful women, and not surprisingly, perhaps, was closed to Europeans by order of the Celestial Emperor. Having travelled by canal boat, he arrived at the city in the evening and tied up on the canal outside the walls for the night. He was woken by a breeze blowing through the cabin window, and it was soon obvious that he had been robbed of almost everything during the night, and cast adrift by the thief. Nevertheless, Fortune now substitued Chinese dress for his own European clothes and, with his head shaved to all but a pigtail, made a passable Chinaman. He was nervous when he entered the city, fearing that he would soon be spotted by the dogs which had an uncanny knack of picking out foreigners, however well disguised; and he recalled bitterly:

> These animals manifest great hatred of foreigners, barking at them whenever they see them and hanging on their skirts until they are fairly out of sight of a house or village where their masters reside.

On a previous occasion he had had to refuse food in an eating house because he feared his clumsiness with chopsticks would reveal him as a fake Chinaman, but in Soochow his disguise passed detection. (Indeed, his appearance was so convincing that when he returned to Shanghai, still wearing his Chinese dress, even his friends failed to recognize him.) Soochow, built on the banks of a canal as broad as the Thames, lived up to its reputation. It was beautiful and prosperous, and ornamented with fine buildings and lakes. The women he encountered were lovely, graceful and most elegantly dressed. He visited nurseries in the city, where he acquired a fine double yellow rose and a gardenia with white blossoms as large as a camellia.

Early in 1845 he made a short trip to Manila in the Philippines to collect orchids, returning to China in late spring to re-collect the finest of the plants he had already despatched to England. He planned to take this second collection back to England personally, to make sure there would be replacements for any of the earlier consignments which might have perished. It consisted mainly of tree paeonies, azaleas, viburnums, daphnes and roses, as well as a considerable number of plants completely new to cultivation in Britain.

Arriving at Chen-hai, he learned that a number of junks were due to leave that evening for Chapu, which was well on his way back to Shanghai. He bought a passage on a small vessel and found himself sharing the centre cabin with a large number of passengers, all of them packed into the small space like sardines. His fellow travellers were unwashed, smelly, and crawling with lice and fleas; and the air was thick with tobacco and opium, which the Chinese smoked late into the night. When dawn broke, all were still, as Fortune described:

> They were lying in heaps, here and there, as they had been tossed and wedged by the motion of the vessel during the night. Their features and appearance, as seen in the twilight of a summer morning, was startling to the eye of a foreigner. I almost fancied that I could read the characters of the different beings who lay stretched before me. There was the habitual opium smoker – there was no mistaking him – his looks were pale and haggard, his breathing quick and disturbed, and so thin was he, that his cheekbones seemed to be piercing his skin. Some seemed care-worn with business, and others again apparently slept soundly with hearts light and joyous. All had the foreparts of their head shaved, and their tails lay about in wild confusion.

At Shanghai he joined up with an Englishman, a Captain Freeman, and together they travelled to Foochow, then the capital of Fukien. Journeying on the River Min, they passed through strikingly beautiful country where the mountains came down almost to the river banks. Some of the lower mountain slopes were terraced into fields growing sweet potatoes and peanuts, while others were barren and rocky. Springs seemed to spout from under every rock, forming streams which in turn became cascades and waterfalls. Thick woods clothed stretches of the banks. Fortune described the Min as 'a beautiful river, winding its way between mountains, its islands, its temples, its villages and fortresses – I think, although not the richest, it is the most romantic and beautiful part of the country which has come under my observation'.

Their reception at Foochow was certainly not as pleasant as the journey. The city was flooded and the streets were under four feet of water, and the two men had to be carried in sedan-chairs to the temple home of the British Consul. As they made their way, their servants were attacked and abused for having anything to do with the devilish foreigners, while they were doused with water. But despite the unfriendliness of the natives, Fortune was able to make some useful additions to his collections from the city's nursery gardens.

Before it was time to start back to Chu-shan, Fortune went down with a severe attack of fever, and for several days he lay in bed slipping in and out of consciousness. He believed he might be destined for a lonely grave on the banks of the Min, and that his only chance was to take passage in a junk that would get him to Chu-shan a great deal faster than the river route.

A small fleet of junks was planning to sail in convoy as a protection against the Jan-dous, the pirates who infested the sea, but despite sailing as a fleet, the captain and crew of his vessel were terrified, and would only take him if he promised to defend them with his guns. Fortune thought that all the talk of pirates was greatly exaggerated. Anyway, he was too ill to care one way or another, and no sooner had he got his baggage aboard than he took to his bunk, weak and shaking from fever.

The junks, most of them laden with timber, set off at a brisk pace, hoping to get well clear of the area before they were spotted by the pirates. Inevitably the fleet soon broke up, leaving the slowest craft alone and most vulnerable to attack. Fortune's vessel was among these slow craft, and at about four o'clock in the afternoon of the first day, when they were some sixty miles from the Min, the captain and pilot burst into his cabin, excitedly shouting that they had spotted a number of pirate ships lying in wait for them. At first Fortune told them to go away, accusing them of seeing every vessel as a pirate, but they were so insistent that he decided he had better see for himself. Having checked his pistols and rammed a ball on top of each charge in the barrels of his double-barrelled shot-gun, he went up on deck, where he saw five junks ahead. They had distinctively raked masts and hulls built more for speed than cargo carrying, and through his pocket telescope he could see that their decks were crowded with men. He no longer doubted they were pirates. The pilot told him that he thought resistance was useless: he might be able to beat off one or two junks with his firearms, but he had no chance against five. But Fortune was determined to put up a fight:

> I knew perfectly well, that if we were taken by the pirates I had not the slightest chance of escape; for the first thing they would do would be to knock me on the head and throw me overboard, as they would deem it dangerous to themselves were I to get away. At the same time I must confess I had little hope of being able to beat off such a number, and devoutly wished myself anywhere rather than where I was.

The captain, crew and other passengers were completely panic-stricken, frantically tearing up the floorboards in the main cabin and hiding their money and valuables in the ballast. Then they brought baskets of small stones out of the ballast onto the deck, so that they could throw them at the pirates when they came to close quarters. This was a common method of defence, but only effective if the enemy also had nothing more than stones, and these pirates were heavily armed.

Having made their token gesture of defiance, the Chinese, much to Fortune's astonishment, now changed into a disgusting array of rags, explaining that the pirates would mistake them for poor men and let them go, rather than hold them for ransom. They were close to hysteria, and pleaded that the junk be turned back to the Min, but with the nearest pirate only two hundred yards away there was no escape. It closed fast, put down its helm and raked the junk with a broadside. Screaming with terror, crew and passengers dived for cover below decks. Only Fortune and two men at the tiller were left to face the attackers, and Fortune had to threaten the helmsmen with his pistols to keep them at their post. The only other defence they had were old clothes, mats and boxes which had been piled against the gunwales.

Every inch of canvas had been raised, and they were moving at top speed, about eight miles an hour. Fortunately the pirate's gunnery was rather haphazard, and the first salvoes fell short, but the vessel had the advantage of speed and was soon close enough for even the most inept gunner to succeed. One shot fell just under the stern, while another howled over their heads and ripped through the sails. The pirates, sure of their prize, closed in, screaming and yelling dementedly and reloading their guns for the kill.

Years afterwards, Fortune could still hear the blood-chilling yells of the pirates as he stood on the deck of the junk, almost alone, facing them. The guns of the nearest pirate ship had been reloaded and it was now within thirty yards and preparing to rake the decks of the merchant vessel. Fortune shouted to his helmsmen to hurl themselves onto the deck the minute they saw him do so. He could see that the pirate must put its helm down to get into the right position to deliver a broadside. As soon as this happened he threw himself down behind a stack of timber while the attackers' shots smashed into the superstructure of the junk. Now the pirate vessel was only twenty yards away and, leaping to his feet, Fortune opened fire with his shot-gun, spraying the pirates with shot and ball. He recorded later:

> Had a thunderbolt fallen among them, they could not have been more surprised. Doubtless many were wounded and probably some killed. At all events, the whole of the crew, not fewer than forty or fifty men, who, a moment before, crowded the deck, disappeared in a marvellous manner; sheltering themselves behind the bulwarks or lying flat on their faces. They were so completely taken by surprise, that their junk was left without a helmsman; her sails flapped in the wind; and, as we were still carrying all sail and keeping on our right course, they were still left at a considerable way astern.

77

With the first pirate out of action, a second Jan-dous vessel swept down on the merchantman, its crew shouting and yelling and all guns firing. Once again Fortune carried out his manoeuvre, but this time he made sure that he shot the helmsman. Two other pirate vessels waiting to take part in the attack, seeing what had happened, steered clear, and this was the signal for the crew and passengers of Fortune's ship to take heart. They rushed up on deck and, with much frenzied shouting, threw stones at the crippled and retreating pirate fleet. As for Fortune, he had become the greatest man in China, and they knelt at his feet in gratitude.

In the heat of the fight he had forgotten his fever, but now it returned and it was all he could do to get back to his cabin. All next day he lay in his bunk as they sailed through peaceful, pirate-free waters, but on the third day out from the Min the captain came to say that another pirate fleet had been sighted and was preparing to attack. Fortune dragged himself on to the deck and through his telescope saw six vessels slipping out from among the islands, and setting a course for the merchant junk.

> After having once seen these rascally vessels, there is no mistaking others of the same class, as they came sneaking out of the bays. Their clipper-built hulls, the cut of their sails, their raking masts, and the crowd of fellows who line their decks, all told the business they were after. It was therefore evident we must prepare for another encounter.

This time Fortune decided to try another tactic, which involved a good deal of bluff. He gathered together all the spare clothes he had and dressed the crew in them, and told them to take hold of the wooden levers used to raise the sails, which, from a distance, he felt sure would be mistaken by the pirates for firearms. By spacing the men about the deck he hoped to create the illusion of a well-armed crew. The plan failed when, with the first salvo from the attackers, his crew threw down the 'guns' and fled below, and again he had to threaten the helmsmen with his pistols to keep them at their post.

With white water at their sharp bows, the pirates bore down, their shot tearing through the merchantman's rigging. The first ship came alongside to deliver the final, disabling broadside. The guns roared, the shots whistled over Fortune and the helmsmen lying flat on the deck, and as before, when the last round had been fired, he leapt to his feet and raked the pirate ship fore and aft with his double-barrelled shot-gun, which was loaded with small shot and ball.

Two other pirate junks closed in and fired a few shots, but their heart was no longer in the fight, and they did not risk coming within range of the European's fire-power. Fortune was also convinced that the success of his shooting had made them believe that there was more than one foreigner aboard. As the night began to close in, the pirates fell back into the darkness, and two hours later the cargo junk reached a safe harbour.

The fever had returned, and Fortune was once again laid low in his bunk. Far from being grateful for all he had done, the captain and crew of the junk treated him in an off-hand manner. The captain came to him and said that he would not now take him to Chu-shan as arranged, but instead he must make his own way to Shanghai from Ningpo; and Fortune had to threaten the man with a loaded pistol in order to get to Chu-shan, from where he sailed to Shanghai.

Robert Fortune eventually recovered from his fever, and left China for England in October 1845, arriving in the Thames in May 1846. His large collection of plants was landed in perfect condition and planted in the Horticultural Society Gardens at Chiswick. Later seeing the plants of *Anemone japonica,* which he had collected, in full flower, he remarked, delightedly, that they were 'as luxuriant and beautiful as it ever grew on the graves of the Chinese, near the ramparts of Shanghai'.

Unable to settle back to an uneventful job in the Chiswick gardens, he returned to China, and also collected in Japan, and with each trip enriched Britain's gardens and greenhouses with plants such as *Primula japonica,* chrysanthemums, the lovely *Deutzia scabra,* as well as azaleas, rhododendrons, forsythia and winter-flowering jasmine.

RICHARD SPRUCE
(1817-92)

Richard Spruce was just about the most unlikely man to be cast in the role of swashbuckling hero and adventurer. Scholarly and retiring, he constantly complained of poor health. Ill at ease with men of the world, he shrank from the idea of being involved in business or commerce. He was completely wedded to botany, and in particular to searching for and studying those least flamboyant of plants, mosses and liverworts. It would have seemed natural for him to have become a parson and devoted his spare time to his favourite group of plants, but, extraordinarily enough, he spent fifteen years of his life, between 1849 and 1864, collecting plants in the Amazon of Brazil and the Andes of Peru and Ecuador.

Richard Spruce was born in 1817 at Ganthorpe, a small village near Castle Howard in Yorkshire, where his father, an outstanding mathematician, was the local schoolmaster. Richard's mother died while he was still a boy, and his father remarried and added eight daughters to the family. Richard was fond of his stepsisters, but he failed to get on with his stepmother.

From childhood he had developed a passion for natural history, and a local naturalist, a Mr G. Stabler, who befriended him, recalled: 'Amongst his favourite amusements was the making of lists of plants.' By the age of sixteen he had listed 403 species that he had collected in the countryside around his home, and three years later he published a list of the flora of the Melton district, which contained 485 species of flowering plants. When he was twenty-four he created excitement among botanists by discovering a British plant new to science, the very rare sedge *Carex paradoxa,* and in the same year found a moss which previously had only been recorded in Lapland. Although an amateur, he was soon recognized as a leading expert on mosses and liverworts (*Hepaticae*), and writing in 1845 in *The Phytologist,* a monthly journal devoted to British botany, he named forty-eight mosses new to the nation's flora.

During the years that he was establishing himself as a botanist, Spruce earned his living as a schoolmaster, an occupation he found irksome. He complained that confinement in the class-room injured his health. However, his life was forced to change when the York Collegiate School, where he taught mathematics, closed. By now he was regularly corresponding with Sir William Hooker and George Bentham, the leading botanists of the day, and he urged them to find him work requiring 'less confinement and less exertion of the lungs than his late engagement and affording botanical pursuits.' Hooker and Bentham suggested that he should set himself up as a plant agent, handling the sale and distribution of collections made by other botanists. Spruce was horrified by this idea: he had to have air and exercise, and would not dream of giving up his own botanical studies. In a letter to Sir William, written in December 1844 when he was twenty-seven, he pleaded, rather pathetically:

> My delicate health and retiring disposition have combined with my love of botanical pursuits to render me fond of solitary study, and I must confess that I feel a sort of shrinking at the idea of engaging in the turmoil of active life.

Despite constant complaints of bilious disorders, gallstones and other illnesses real and imagined, the following year he set off for the Pyrenees, where he spent a year collecting, often walking thirty miles a day and setting such a pace that his guides were left flagging in his tracks. At one stage he disappeared and the local police were enlisted to search for him. They could find no trace of him, but in the end he emerged with a magnificent collection of mosses, liverworts and other plants.

Spruce appears to have had a split personality. On the one hand there was the hypochondriac wallowing, where one suspects that his many ailments and complaints were suffered not without some pleasure, and on the other the dedicated botanist prepared to face any kind of hardship to find and collect plants new to science.

When it was decided that he should go to South America to collect in the Amazon forest and the Andes, the vapours struck again. The strain of packing his bags and equipment brought on bilious attacks, and he had to submit to blistering. That he was anxious about the trip was understandable: he had no official backing and had to finance the entire undertaking by making collections of herbarium specimens to be sold to private collectors. He had contracts with twenty clients, which meant that he had to collect twenty sets of every plant discovered, as well as material for his own use, and describe each set with full field notes. Eventually his clientele rose to thirty, which involved an enormous amount of work, for which he received only £2 per hundred specimens.

In June 1849 Spruce set sail from Liverpool, and twenty-five days later he arrived in Pará at the mouth of the Amazon (despite being run onto a rock by a drunken pilot). He immediately set about collecting in the country around Pará, and by November had moved on to Santarém, where he had heard that the giant Victoria water-lily could be found in flower in a forest lake. His first sight of its huge raft-like leaves and the fully opened flowers produced a childlike reaction: he plunged into the water to count the leaves and tow specimens ashore, despite warnings that the leaves were armed with vicious thorns. Writing to Sir William Hooker, he said:

> We were warned by the people not to go amongst the plants as their prickles were enormous, our legs, both

hands and feet, were considerably pricked without experiencing any ill-effects.

The aspect of the *Victoria* in its native waters is so new and extraordinary, that I am at a loss what to compare it to.

In 1852, at São Gabriel on the Rio Negro, he came face to face with the Amazon's greatest and most dangerous hazard – people. There were few civilians living in the town, and the garrison of fourteen men was made up of criminals, half of them murderers, who were serving their sentences in the army. When he left his house to collect plants in the surrounding country, his rum and provisions were stolen by the soldiers who were supposed to be maintaining the peace. The alertness he learned in this rough settlement, and his knowledge of the local languages, were to prove vital, and certainly saved him from the would-be murderers who were to plot his death two years later.

In 1853, at San Carlos del Negro in Venezuela, the first serious threat to his life occurred. He arrived in the town shortly before the Feast of St John, to be told that the Indians planned to massacre all the white population on the day of the Feast. Indians from the forest had come in to join the so-called shirted Indians, those who lived in the settlements, and were working up their courage with the local rum, forcing their way into European houses and demanding the spirit. Most of the whites fled, but Spruce, who was sharing a house with two young Portuguese, decided to stay.

There was no hope of any help from the chief of police and his men, because they too had run away, so every night Spruce and the Portuguese barricaded themselves indoors and mounted an armed guard. Outside in the streets the drunken Indians hurled insults and threats. The Feast-day of St John dawned quietly and, apart from some brawling among the Indians, there was little of the aggression of the previous days. The two Portuguese were convinced that this was the quiet before the storm, and that the Indians were conserving their energies for the massacre, but Spruce disagreed, and to prove his point took down the barricades and stood in the open doorway of the house, a pistol in each hand.

The Indians eyed the strange figure nervously. Strikingly tall
and thin, and heavily tanned, his gaunt, intense face framed by
long honey-coloured hair and a whispy, unkempt beard, he must
have been a daunting sight. No one dared approach him, and as
evening drew near the Indians quietly slipped away into
the forest.

Shortly after this incident, Spruce set off up the Orinoco river
for Esmeralda, a tiny township close to the 8000-feet high Duida
mountain, with the intention of collecting plants on its summit.
Esmeralda looked beautiful, a tropical paradise, but, he wrote in a
letter home, 'in reality it is an inferno scarcely habitable by man.'
When he first arrived in the town he was struck by a deadly
silence, as he stood in the square surrounded by the six houses
that made up the settlement. The straw doors were fast closed
and the only movement was the dust stirred by the warm wind.
There was not a sound, or even any evidence of life, not a bird,
not a butterfly. But all around there was a rich profusion of plant
life, lush and varied. Spruce was mystified, but when he put his
hand to his face to wipe away the sweat – the heat was as oppressive as the silence – he found it was instantly covered with blood
and the crushed bodies of gorged mosquitoes. The settlement
was infested with the insects, and the inhabitants had to spend
the days locked in their houses, only daring to come out at night.

Spruce had to work during the day, and each time he returned
from a collecting trip his hands, feet, neck and face would all be
covered with blood. He could not sit down to eat, but had to walk
about, plate in hand, the food crawling with mosquitoes. When
he worked on his plants he wore gloves and tied his trousers at
the ankles, but even so the insects penetrated his clothes, bit him
unmercifully, and left him with blood streaming from a mass of
minute punctures. 'If I climbed the cerros, or buried myself
in the forest or sought the centre of the savannas, it was the same;
but it was worst of all on the river', he recalled.

It was hardly surprising, therefore, that on his way back down
the Orinoco river, in the middle of 1854, he was seized by a
severe attack of fever. He managed to reach the Maipures
Mission where, for thirty-eight days, he hung between life and

death, his life threatened not only by fever but also by the vicious old harridan hired to nurse him. He had no proper medicines with him, and his so-called nurse was anxious to hurry him to his grave so that she could rob him of his bag of dollars. Delirious with fever, Spruce moved into the woman's house, but it soon became evident that she intended to do nothing to relieve his suffering. At night, when the attacks were most violent, she would ignore him, except to mock him from her seat on the verandah, shouting: 'Die, you English dog, that we may have a merry valorio [watch night] with your dollars!'

One night he was so ill that he was sure he would die before dawn. Seeing his condition, the woman locked him in the house and went off with her family until after midnight. They were furious when they found him on their return still alive, and he overheard a whispered conversation in which it was planned to poison his gruel. He dared not sleep, and in fact only dozed off three times in twenty days and, now that he was threatened with poisoning, dared not eat. Reduced almost to a skeleton, he was so convinced he would die that, with a superhuman effort, he wrote a will.

To his own surprise, and to the rage of his nurse, he rallied, threw off the fever and recovered, but there is no doubt that the attack left its mark on him. As he said in a letter to Sir William Hooker at the beginning of January 1855: 'The Venezuelans say very expressively that however completely a man may think he has thrown off the ague, there always remains a bit of it sticking to his backbone.'

By now Spruce had spent five years working and living deep in the Amazon, and the forest must have held few fears for him, even at night when the dense cover of foliage would come alive with a weird symphony of shrieks, hoots, whistles, grunts and roars. He was at ease with the beautiful, and often strange, birds and animals that inhabited the trees and plants that he loved above all else, and had now learned to tolerate the incessant whine and painful bite of the mosquito swarms that plagued the river banks.

On the night of 23 November 1854, as he lay in his hammock

slung beneath a rough thatch of leaves, the jungle sounds were soothing, and the slight breeze that blew in through the open sides of the shelter was cooling. He had only just recovered from his severe attack of fever which had left him pallid and listless, but he was glad to be back in the wilderness. As he listened to the night noises he became aware of the sound of voices, rising and growing more excited in the shelter next to his. They came from his canoe crew, an old man and his three sons, who were squatting in a tight triangle drinking *bureche*, which was a fiery, home-brewed rum.

Spruce had hired his crew at the last minute, and it had been the old man who insisted on the night stop, explaining that he owned the property and that they would be comfortable there. In fact it was where he kept his still and he wanted to check that his latest brew had come to no harm. At first their talking had been little more than another sound blending in with others, but as the rum took hold Spruce could hear them clearly. They were plotting a murder – his murder.

The old man spoke while his sons listened. The white man had been very ill in San Carlos so it would come as no surprise to people when they heard he had died. Anyway, he was on his way to his own country and would never return to the Amazon, so he would not be missed. There was dense forest between them and the river, so no one would see the killing. They had been paid in advance, and there were probably great riches to be found in the white man's bags and boxes. 'Besides this', Spruce wrote in his journal, 'they discussed the disposal of the body, and themselves, after committing the crime, with a degree of skill and forethought which would have done credit to the most practised assassins'.

Brave with rum, the Indians were about to see whether Spruce was asleep when he climbed out of his hammock and indicated that he was going to relieve himself in the thick bushes. Once out of sight he hurried to the canoe, barricaded himself in the cabin, and waited for the attack, armed with a loaded gun and a cutlass. When he did not return the Indians started to search for him. He could hear them crashing drunkenly through the undergrowth and shouting to one another. The next morning, when they shambled down to the canoe, they shrank back at the sight of the tall, thin Englishman, the glint of fever still in his eyes, levelling a loaded shot-gun at their chests. Not knowing that he understood the Barre language they spoke, they were mystified by the fact that he had detected their plot, and throughout the remainder of the journey to Manaos he had no further trouble. But to make sure, his gun never left his side.

Having avoided two attempts on his life in 1854, Spruce no doubt hoped that 1855 would be less hazardous, but it was not to be. That year there was gold fever on the Upper Marañon, and with it came an army of prospectors, mainly English and American. Some of them were genuine, but the majority appear to have been adventurers and criminals on the run. The reports of gold proved to be false, and the would-be miners turned to crime and violence in order to survive. Many were murdered by the Indians they mistreated.

One of these prospectors was Charles Nelson, an Englishman who had been a sailor and a digger in Australia. He seemed a steady, quiet fellow and Spruce hired him to accompany him to Peru. In a letter from Yurimaguas in the Province of Maynas, Peru, he explained that he took Nelson on 'thinking that a stout companion like him would be invaluable to me in a country where (as report truly said) there was no law but that of the strongest'. What he did not know was that Nelson had been in prison in Peru for murder, and had left a trail of violence and mayhem right across the country. He was also a paranoiac and, being deaf, held the persecuted belief that anyone who laughed was poking fun at him. At first he had seemed an ideal companion – resourceful, hardworking and willing. But when they reached Peru, where there was no proper law and order, his attitude changed. He became sullen and aggressive, and it became increasingly evident to Spruce that Nelson was merely waiting for an opportunity to murder and rob him.

His behaviour became more violent and unpredictable when they arrived at Yurimaguas. He savagely beat an elderly Indian, and the following day when he, Spruce and a Portuguese were dining with the local priest, he went berserk. The Portuguese had been telling a story that caused laughter, which Nelson thought was directed at him. Snatching up a pick-axe handle, he attacked the Portuguese, who fled into another room and bolted the door, which the sailor tried to kick down. Somehow the priest and Spruce managed to calm the man, who was now making such open threats against Spruce that for several days the botanist slept with a pistol under his pillow. Eventually Spruce got rid of him by paying him three months' wages and buying him a passage to Barra. (He never made his destination, but was murdered by his Indian boatmen.)

Despite the hardship, danger and disease that Spruce had to contend with during his years in South America, he never ceased to display an almost childish delight in the wonderful profusion of plants, animals and insects that surrounded him. In letters and in his journal, he described the plants of the Amazon basin with exuberance:

> There were enormous trees, crowned with magnificent foliage, decked with fantastic parasites, hung over with lianas which varied in thickness from slender threads to huge, python-like masses, rounded, flattened, twisted with the regularity of a cable . . . here our grasses are bamboos sixty or more feet high . . . our milkweeds are stout woody twiners, ascending to the highest top of trees . . . instead of your perriwinkles, we have handsome trees exuding a most deadly poison. Violets are the size of apple trees.

He was also enchanted by a psittacanthi of the open pampas, which 'has handsome yellow flowers of the most delicious odour, like that of honeysuckle, but stronger – after a shower the campos are sometimes quite perfumed by it'. It was, however, his collection of the seeds and plants of the quinine-bearing chinchona tree that was to have the most far-reaching effect. Quinine, for years the most effective source of the antidote to malaria, had been known in Europe for more than 200 years but, because of its great value, successive Peruvian administrations had refused to allow seeds or plants to be exported.

The curative properties of the tree had been discovered in 1638 when the wife of the Viceroy of Peru, Doña Francisca Henriques de Rivera, Countess of Chinchon, was struck down by malaria on a journey to Quito. In despair, her physician sought the aid of Inca medicine men who told him to administer the powdered bark of the tree. The cure was almost instantaneous, and when Doña Francisca returned to Spain she took a quantity of the bark with her, and for many years it was known as the 'Countess's Powder'. Her physician also took home a large supply, which he sold at a handsome profit to his patients, for in those days malaria was a common disease in Europe.

Jesuit missionaries later exported the bark to Europe, and it became known as 'Jesuit's Bark', with the consequence that Protestants refused to touch it on the grounds that it was in some way tainted with Popery. However, its efficacy overcame prejudice, and chinchona became a vital element in many medicines. The gathering of the bark of the chinchona trees grew into a prosperous industry, and as a result the Peruvian authorities resisted all attempts by foreigners to gather seeds or plants for cultivation elsewhere.

Spruce recognized that the trees could be grown successfully in other tropical areas such as those of the British Empire, where malaria caused havoc among both native and European populations, and that to have an adequate home-grown supply had obvious advantages. Through a British Government agent, Spruce offered to collect seeds and plants for cultivation in the Eastern colonies, but the initial response from London was negative.

Although annoyed and disappointed, he was happy enough with his normal work. For three years his base was Tarapoto, a hill town in Peru, where he was fondly known as Don Ricardo by the local people, who would consult him whenever they had a problem. He walked in the forest with the Indians, discussing their herbal remedies, and his evenings were spent playing chess with the parish priest. The tranquillity of his life was disturbed for a time when revolution broke out, as a result of a General Vivanco trying to oust the President, General Catillo. The natives fled with their possessions into the forests and plains, to avoid being press-ganged into the forces of either side. When the Vivanco army arrived and began ransacking houses, Spruce loaded his revolver and double-barrelled shot-gun, and unleashed his formidable dog, Sultan, a fine, handsome animal who protected his master from all comers. With a combination of threats and firmness, he was able to persuade the soldiers to leave him alone. But in March 1857 he wrote: 'I am still a prisoner here, what with the revolutions on the one hand which render the sierra unsafe to pass, and with the swollen river on the other'.

Eventually, word reached him at Tarapoto that Her Majesty's Secretary of State for India had decided to commission him to travel to the forests of Andean Ecuador to study the chinchona trees, and to collect the seeds and seedlings of those trees he judged best suited for growing in plantations in the East. Soon after receiving the news he set off on what was to prove the toughest and most hazardous expedition of his career – 560 miles by canoe to Canelos, first on the Huallaga and then the Marañon rivers, branching off to the Pastaza and Bombanaza, and thus deep into the high Andes. His destination was the region round the Sangay volcano, which is overlooked by the towering snow-capped peak of Chimborazo fifty miles to the north.

Long stretches of the rivers were made deadly by huge jagged rocks, rapids and whirlpools. On the Huallaga the expedition nearly foundered when the canoe was sucked into a whirlpool. When the boat plunged into the maelstrom, Spruce's dog Sultan was standing in the prow. Only a few days before they left Tarapoto the dog had pulled down a deer, but now he was terrified by the deafening roar of the water and the waves and spray breaking over the canoe. Although they soon reached safety, he never recovered from the experience, and helplessly Spruce had to stand by and watch the animal pine away. In a letter to George Bentham, the botanist who handled the sales of his herbarium specimens, Spruce wrote of the dog he had reared from a puppy:

From that hour he would drink no water and after the first day would take no food. Six days I kept him by my side at great personal risk hoping to cure him. When we went on shore in the villages he ran straight off uttering the most unearthly sounds and putting to flight dogs, pigs and cows – sometimes biting them severely. At length he began to snap at the people in the canoe and being worn almost to a skeleton, I saw all hope of saving him was in vain and was obliged to shoot him.

The remainder of the river journey was made increasingly difficult by torrential rain and floods, but conditions were luxurious compared with those of the overland trek to come.

They left the Bombanaza to march to a group of three Indian villages, Sara-Ucu, Paca-Yacu and Canelos, hoping to find the local Governor and arrange porters to complete the journey to the chinchona forests. The Governor was found in Paca-Yacu, two-and-a-half days' journey below Canelos, where they were kept waiting three weeks for porters. When they did eventually start out, they found the forests in the Canelos area (which had proved such a hazard to the explorers Gonzalez Pizarro and Orelano three hundred years before) even wilder than in the days of the Conquistadores, because they were now completely uninhabited. Any roads that had existed had long ago disappeared, and they had to follow animal tracks, hanging on to tree-roots as they groped their way across cliff-faces. Spruce wrote:

> The rains set in with greater severity than ever – the dripping forest through which I had to push my way, soaking my garments so that towards evening my arms and shoulders were quite benumbed – and the mud, which even on the tops of the hills was often over the knees – make our progress very slow and painful.

When they reached the Topo river, expecting a reasonably shallow, easily fordable stream, they found it swollen by floods into a raging torrent. For two days and nights they camped on the bank waiting for its level to drop, but it continued to roar past,

91

wide and furious. Their stores ran out and, since they were dangerously close to starving, they decided to build a makeshift bridge of bamboo canes lashed together. Forty feet long and very fragile, the bridge almost broke under the weight of a single man without a load. It was impossible to take Spruce's heavy trunks and boxes across, so they were left under a thatched shelter. (When they were recovered some time later, the thatch had collapsed and the leather covering of the trunks was alive with maggots, but the contents were hardly damaged.) Spruce did manage to get his bedding and clothes across, but by the time that had been achieved there were clear signs of another imminent flood, and barely had the last man crossed safely than the bridge was swept away.

Endlessly soaked through, the botanist suffered so severely from catarrh and coughs that he sometimes bled from both his nose and mouth. But he pressed on, cautiously passing through the country of the notorious head-hunting Jivaros, whom he met and found friendly. When he finally reached Ambato in Ecuador, his troubles were still not at an end. Inevitably, a revolution was in progress, and there had been a major battle on the slopes of Chimborazo. First the defeated forces came through the town, shortly followed by the victors. The local people had fled into the surrounding forest, taking with them all their household goods, even the glass from their windows, rather than let it fall into the hands of looting soldiers. Spruce stayed here, largely because he was recovering from fever, and anyway had nowhere else to go. He laid in a stock of food, ran up a Union Jack and prepared for a siege, but his house 'was respected, and neither horses nor anything else molested', he recorded gratefully.

During his marathon journey he had made an important collection of plants, particularly ferns and mosses, which he discovered by wading in freezing streams to gather them from rocks and crevices. Now he was close to the chinchona forests, but every obstacle was put in the way of his aim of collecting from them. In the end he managed to rent a forest, and set about training a group of collectors, but his careful plans were nearly wrecked when local people, hearing that the strange Englishman wanted seeds of the chinchona, stripped some of the best trees before the seeds were ripe and offered to sell them to him. In addition to this, for several weeks his collecting was interrupted by troops of the Provisional Government of Quito marching down from the sierra to attack revolutionary forces. His hand-picked team of eleven collectors, whom he had carefully trained, were pressed into the army, and in the end he had to make do with four untrained Indians.

As if these were not problems enough, his health broke down. He was unable to sit at a table to work for any length of time, and did most of his writing and reading in a hammock. He suffered from a kind of intermittent paralysis in his arms and legs which caused him to collapse if he was walking, or fall from a horse if he was riding. At the same time he lost his meagre savings – £700 – which he had invested in a company in Guayaquil, which went bankrupt. It was hardly surprising that he wrote this gloomy and bitter letter to a friend, David Hanbury:

> ... I have met many men who, beginning without a cent, made more money in two or three years than I have in thirteen, and that without being exposed to thunderstorms and pelting rain, and sitting in a canoe up to the knees in water, eating of bad and scanty food once a day, getting no sleep at night from the attacks of venomous insects, to say nothing of the certainty of having every now and then to look death in the face, as I have done.

A lesser man might have given up what certainly seemed to be an unequal struggle, but Spruce pressed on with his chinchona commission, collecting 2500 well-grown capsules of seed, 2000 from trees at Limon and 500 from five trees at San Antonio – altogether some 100,000 clean, ripe seeds. He also raised a large batch of seedlings which he took to Guayaquil on the coast by rafts, and eventually freighted to England from Ecuador on 2 January 1861.

It was a superb achievement, but Spruce was a broken and

disappointed man. He had appealed for some kind of official British Government appointment in South America, which would have paid him a small income, allowing him to continue his botanical work without the arduous drudgery of mass collecting to support himself and his expeditions. No appointment was offered. He saw himself dying of fever and poverty in the marshes of Guayaquil, never able to return to England to spend his remaining years working on his collections and enjoying the company and esteem of his fellow scientists. In a letter written at Chinana, near Guayaquil, in October 1861, he gave vent to his bitterness: 'Had I worked as long in the East as I have done in the West, I might have reasonably calculated on a small pension when I was disabled from working; but I do not suppose there is any hope of such a thing in my case.'

Three years later he did return home to England. By then the chinchona plantations in the Neilgherry Hills of southern India and in Sri Lanka were developing from the plants and seeds he had collected. The pharmaceutical industry was set to make a fortune out of processing the bark, and untold thousands of lives were saved from the scourge of malaria. As if this were not achievement enough, he also collected over 30,000 specimens of plants, gathered vocabularies of Indian languages and dialects, mapped 10,000 miles of river, and produced a detailed study of rubber trees and related latex-bearing trees that was to prove invaluable to the rubber industry in the Far East, when, twenty years later, Henry A. Wickham collected seeds of the rubber tree at Santarém.

Eventually, and rather reluctantly, the British Government and the Indian administration agreed to pay Spruce a joint pension of £100 a year. This niggardly allowance enabled him to retire to a tiny cottage at Coneythorpe in Yorkshire, where he worked up his collections and wrote his monumental scientific classic, *Hepaticae Amazonicae et Andinea,* published in 1885, in which he described over 700 species of liverwort, 500 of which he had collected. He also wrote a popular account of his journeys. Despite ill-health, he lived to the age of seventy-five, dying three days after Christmas in 1892.

The American botanist Richard Evans Schultes, writing in the magazine *The Northern Gardener,* composed an apt epitaph for Spruce:

> I have felt it in the deep shadow of the Amazonian forest and in the blinding brightness of the Amazonian waters; I have felt it in herbaria; I felt it whilst standing before Spruce's humble cottage in the hamlet of Coneythorpe; I felt it again when I stood reverently before Spruce's grave in the churchyard at Terrington; but there, under the lowering sky of a Yorkshire April, I knew it to be true: Richard Spruce still lives, and will live to fire the hearts and shape the thoughts of many a plant explorer as yet unborn, who will tread Spruce's trail to carry forward his great, unfinished work.

JOSEPH HOOKER
(1817-1911)

Joseph Dalton Hooker was brought up surrounded by talk about botany and plants, particularly the new plants which were beginning to flood into Britain. His father, William Hooker, who had been to Iceland as a plant collector, became Professor of Botany at Glasgow University in 1820, and in the years that followed Joseph heard a great deal about the wonderful discoveries being made, particularly in Britain's expanding empire. It was scarcely surprising, therefore, that when William moved south to become Director of Kew, his son was inspired to become a collector for the Gardens.

He was the ideal plant-hunting type – courageous, energetic, resourceful and intelligent; possessing that curiously Victorian arrogance, bordering on contempt, towards foreigners, that served as a life-preserver for so many British explorers. He was convinced of his perfect right to be wherever he chose, and never had the slightest doubt that he was the correct person to carry out his commission, which was to hunt for plants in the then little-known Himalayas, the great mountain range looming magnificently over the Indian Empire.

Joseph, who eventually followed his father as Director of Kew, began his career as an explorer in 1839, at the age of twenty two, when he was appointed naturalist on Captain James Clark Ross's Arctic expedition, a voyage of great hardship and danger. By contrast, the start of his expedition to the Himalayas in 1848 was positively luxurious. He set off overland from Calcutta on 28 January with a baggage train made up of bullocks, bullock carts and elephants, while he rode in a 'palkee', a box-like vehicle hauled by men. He soon tired of this, though, when the heat inside the swaying, jerking box with its closed shutters became unendurable, and before long he transferred to an elephant; but he was shocked and disgusted at the way the animal was treated by its mahout (elephant-driver), who hammered at the creature's head with an iron goad. He wrote in a letter home, 'A most disagreeable sight it is, to see the blood and yellow fat oozing out in the broiling sun'. (His elephant had its revenge by charging into a village, scattering the people and wrecking a food stall.)

On reaching Mirzapur on the Ganges he hired a rather shabby boat whose cabin was thatched with grass, so that it looked like a floating haystack. It was forty feet long and fifteen wide, and only drew a foot and a half of water; the deck was barely above the water level. On 21 March he set off upriver for Bhagalpur, stopping at Patna to study the manufacture of opium. Here he was shown a plant – the 'Murdar Plant' (*Caloptris*) – which was credited with remarkable healing powers, including the cure of leprosy. It was a pleasant, uneventful voyage except that on 9 April a tremendous wind-storm sent them scuttling for the shelter of the bank, which the vessel bumped, springing several leaks. The only relatively dry place was the cabin used by Hooker, and here he was joined by disturbed rats and cockroaches that set about eating his stores, which had already been spoiled by the sand stirred up in the gale.

At Bhagalpur Hooker left the river and made his way overland to Darjeeling, arriving on 16 April. It became his home for the next two years, and it was from this base that he collected the spectacular rhododendrons of Sikkim for which he is best remembered. The mountains around Darjeeling were beautiful and rich with plants, but not always comfortable for travellers. One of his earliest experiences of mountain life in the foothills of the Himalayas was when he had to spend a night in a bungalow, which he described as:

> . . . the most sinister looking rest-house I ever saw,
> stuck on a little cleared spur of the mountains, surrounded
> by dark forests, over-hanging a profound valley, and
> enveloped in mists and rain, and hideous in architecture,
> being a miserable attempt to unite the Swiss cottage with
> the suburban gothic; it combined a maximum of discom-
> fort with the minimum of good looks or good cheer.

Although he had arrived in Darjeeling in the rainy season,
which inhibited his movements, any sense of discouragement
he had felt disappeared at his first sight of Indian rhododendrons.
He found *Rhododendron dalhousiae* growing epiphytically in a
wood, its white, lemon-scented bell-shaped flowers hanging
from every branch. In the same wood was *Rhododendron
arboreum,* rich with scarlet flowers, and *Rhododendron argenteum*
(now listed as *Rhododendron grande*) growing forty feet high,
with leaves more than a foot long, and huge ivory-white flowers.
Hooker climbed through woods full of towering specimens such
as the crimson-flowered *Rhododendron barbatum, Rhododendron
arboreum var. roseum,* and *Rhododendron hodgsonii* with its striking foliage and magenta flowers; and in the mountains of
neighbouring Nepal he discovered *Rhododendron anthopogon*
and *Rhododendron setosum,* two alpine species with scented
foliage.

The mountains became an endless source of enchantment
for Hooker. In his Himalayan journal he described looking down
on the mist swirling through the valleys beneath him:

> I saw a sea of mist floating 3000 feet beneath me, just
> below the upper level of the black pines; the magnificent
> spurs of the snowy mountains which I had crossed rising
> out of it in rugged grandeur as promontories and pen-
> insulas, between which the misty oceans seem to finger
> up like the fiords of Norway, or the salt-water lochs of
> the West of Scotland; vast islets tailed off from the
> promontories, rising here and there out of the deceptive
> elements. I was so high above this mist, that it had not the
> billowy appearance it had before, but was a calm un-
> ruffled ocean, boundless to the south and west, where the
> horizon over-arched it.

Some months later, when he was collecting in the north of Sikkim on the Tibetan frontier, he experienced the unearthly atmospheric phenomenon sometimes called The Spectre of the Brocken – 'my own shadow being projected on a mass of thin mist that rose above the tremendous precipice over which I hung. My head was surrounded by a brilliant circular glory or rainbow'.

But mountain-climbing was not always so romantically beautiful. In a letter from Darjeeling dated 26 April 1848, he complained of having to wait three days at the foot of a mountain for his porters to bring up his baggage. He had no dry clothes or any paper for the plants he had collected. The mountainside was covered with thick forest and the trees constantly dripped from the moisture of the fogs that swirled through them. One minute it was hot, the next cold; and the path was so steep that he could not leave it if he rode his pony, so he abandoned the comfort of riding in order to be able to botanize:

> . . . diving into little gullies, and coming out loaded with new plants and ferns, and my legs with leeches, which swarm about the foot of the hills, bite through your stockings and roll themselves up into little balls like thick-skinned gooseberries, and thus lie with impunity within your shoes.

He was without a tent, and so he slept under the shelter of a precipice to try to get some protection from the lashing rain and snow. But in the morning the weather was glorious, and his view on waking was the sunlit peaks of the mountains of the Kinchin group – 'peak after peak with cliffs, domes and tables of snow, it really conveyed the idea of a forest of mountains', he wrote. At eight in the morning the clouds began to roll up, and by nine the scene had disappeared in a blanket of fog. An hour later, rain, sleet and snow were lashing down, and continued to do so throughout the day and the following night. When his porters eventually arrived, he had to send them back down 2000 feet to collect firewood, which was soaked by the time they had brought it up. The wet wood, combined with the thinness of the atmosphere, meant that it was almost impossible to kindle a fire.

Although he was surrounded by at least fifty porters and collectors, Hooker's closest companion was a dog he named Kinchin, which he had brought with him to Sikkim as a puppy. A cross between a Tibetan mastiff and the common Sikkim hunting dog (closely related to the pariah dogs of the plains), it grew into a fine large animal with a thick, glossy black coat and a splendid plumed tail. The two were inseparable companions, and Hooker's affection for the animal can be seen in the sketches and cartoons of Kinchin in his field notebooks. Sadly, one day when they were crossing a bamboo bridge over a river, the dog became panic-stricken, slipped and, before Hooker was able to haul the animal to safety, plunged into the fast-flowing torrent, was swept away and drowned. 'For many days I missed him by my side on the mountain, and by my feet in the camp', Hooker wrote in his journal.

Hooker often felt lonely and isolated, particularly after his frequent companion Dr Archibald Campbell, the political agent in Darjeeling, had to leave him in the mountains. He wrote:

> It is quite impossible for anyone who cannot from experience realise the solitary wandering life I have been leading for months, to appreciate the desolate feeling that follows the parting from one who has heightened every enjoyment, taken far more than his share of annoyance and discomfort.

In Sikkim, in particular, there were no lack of annoyances. The Rajah was very reluctant to allow Hooker into the country, and his opposition was supported by some of the monks, or lamas, who even went so far as to destroy bridges in order to impede his progress. The Tibetan villagers told him not to shoot in the area, as they said shots would induce excessive rain and ruin their crops. Since Hooker had to hunt in order to eat, he decided to ignore the order, until a leading local lama was brought to plead with him. This was, he felt sure, just another ploy to encourage him to leave the country. Strict instructions had in fact been issued that neither he nor his party were to be supplied with any food, but because he tended the sick in the villages, food was brought to him under cover of darkness. Even this clandestine help was not enough, however, after a party bringing them stores was halted by a landslide. With only a kid, a few handfuls of flour and some potatoes for food, Hooker's position was desperate. Eventually one bag of rice got through with the message that there was more on the way, but for nearly a week Hooker and his men had to survive on what they could find – wild leeks, nettles and herbs.

The problems of survival were nevertheless outweighed by the treasury of plants that surrounded him. There were rhododendrons 'glowing with bells of brilliant colours', and a profusion of primulas, from three-foot 'yellow cowslips' (undoubtedly the lovely scented *Primula sikkimensis*) and purple and pink species, to 'an exquisitely beautiful blue miniature species, whose blossoms sparkle like sapphires on the turf'. There were also gentians and aconites, fritillaries and blue poppies (*Meconopsis*), and a magnificent rhubarb, *Rheum nobile*.

Having failed to starve him out, the natives next tried intimidation. A gang of them appeared and threw Hooker's collectors out of their huts, along with the plants they were preserving, the paper and boards for the presses, and their instruments. At night the villagers' dogs were turned loose to howl at the moon, and on one occasion made off with Hooker's supply of meat. In addition, the yaks which grazed on the mountainside were inclined to burst into the tents at night, awakening him 'with a snort and moist hot blast'. In the end he had to build a turf wall round his tent as protection against them, and keep a heavy tripod to hand to prod the beasts away from him. But at least the yaks were a valuable source of protein, and for quite a time he survived on dried yak meat, which he found a great deal more palatable than the local mutton, which, he complained, tasted of tallow and was impossible to eat.

Hooker was a fastidious eater and found oriental cooking distasteful. In a letter to Nathaniel Wallich, the Danish botanist employed by the East India Company, he declared: 'In only one thing am I deceived by all you Indians in England; and that is the cookery – which is in every respect villainous

and atrocious. Your stews, pilafs and curries I abhor and eschew.'
And he had nothing good to say about the local wine either.
Nevertheless, in the autumn of 1849 he must have had cause
to yearn for the curries, stews and pilafs, however atrocious.
He and Dr Campbell were making an expedition from Sikkim
into Tibet and back. The Tibetans were not enthusiastic about
the intrusion and allowed them to spend only one day over the
border, and the Sikkimese did not want them back in their
country. The main cause of their problems was the deep dislike of
Campbell by the Rajah of Sikkim's chief adviser, the Dewan.
The Rajah was a weak and foolish man, and Campbell had lost
no time in spotting the Dewan as a villain, determined to grow
rich on the gullibility of his master.

Campbell suffered from a widespread belief that he was
something of an incompetent, and clearly Hooker had at first
been convinced of this, because in an early letter home he
described him as 'a curious compound, the weakest political
resident perhaps in the service; giving in to this imbecile and
crafty Rajah in everything'. It was a false judgement, as events
were to prove. Campbell was clever, subtle and brave, and, as
Hooker later gladly admitted, 'a capital companion'.

On 7 November 1849, when every other means had failed to
turn Hooker and Campbell out of Sikkim, the Dewan struck.
That night it was bitterly cold, and Campbell and Hooker had
gone into a hut to rest and warm themselves. Hardly had they
settled down than a large number of Sikkimese crowded into the
hut after them. Campbell, thinking it better to leave the building
to the people, went outside to supervise the pitching of the
tents, but no sooner had he left than Hooker heard him yelling,
'Hooker! Hooker! the savages are murdering me!'

Hooker pushed his way through the crowd to the door, to see
Campbell desperately trying to defend himself against a mob
of men. Being tall, powerfully built and extremely fit, he had
knocked down a few, but there were so many that their weight
alone had forced him down to the ground, where he was being
kicked and trampled upon. Hooker was instantly seized by
several others, pushed back into the hut and forced down onto

the log on which he had been sitting. His struggles were of little use as there were about twenty-five men in the hut and he was pinned against the wall. In the background he could hear Campbell's stifled cries growing fainter, and it seemed as if his companion was being killed, except for the fact that none of the men attacking him had been carrying a weapon. If assassination had been the plan, Hooker reasoned, then an arrow would have been a surer and less troublesome way of disposing of him.

The Dewan wanted to create a lasting breach with the British, and to mistreat an officer of the Crown was as good a way as any to destroy relationships between the two countries. The Dewan's motive was pure greed. He was not even a Sikkimese, but a Tibetan relative of the Rajah's wife, and he had seized the monopoly of the trade in and out of Sikkim. Internally he could defend his position with his private army made up of convicted felons who had fled from British territory, but it was essential to exclude any foreigners who might break his monopoly. Campbell had been working successfully for the downfall of the Dewan, which was why he had to be got out of the way, but not before the Tibetan had brutally exacted his revenge.

Once on the ground, Campbell was kicked and beaten about the head, then one of the men seized his head and bent it so ferociously that he thought they wanted to break his neck. Bleeding and battered, he was dragged to a hut and tortured. His arms were doubled up behind his back, and he was shaken to and fro at the end of a rope. Lengths of bamboo were inserted under the ropes binding him, and twisted until it seemed as though the bonds would cut through his flesh to the bone. A bow was shaken in his face, while another man made throat-cutting gestures in front of him.

Hooker, meanwhile, was interrogated, but not threatened with violence. All his questioners wanted to know was how he thought Campbell would react to his treatment, but Hooker refused to answer any questions until his own arrest had been explained. The following morning, to his relief, he was taken to see Campbell, who was limping badly and heavily bruised about the face, but otherwise none the worse for his ordeal.

His greatest concern was not for himself but for his wife in Darjeeling, who was expecting a baby at any moment.

From here Hooker and Campbell were taken under heavy guard to Tumlong. Campbell was now further humiliated by being dragged along at the tail of a mule. Hooker was offered a pony but indignantly refused to ride it, and instead walked as close to his friend as he was allowed. Even under these difficult circumstances, he managed to snatch ripe capsules of rhododendron seed from the bushes they passed, and in fact made an impressive collection of seeds of many different species.

At Tumlong they were again separated, and Campbell was put under lock and key. Hooker was offered a hut so filthy and verminous that he decided to stay in a tent pitched nearby. Gifts of a large cow, sheep, fowls, tea, bags of rice, flour, butter, eggs and vegetables were all brought to him, in an attempt to win his approval, but he would accept them only as provisions. For several days the two men were thus isolated from one another, managing to keep in touch by means of messages smuggled between them by Hooker's porters, but eventually Hooker was allowed to join Campbell in his bamboo and mud hut, which had two wretched rooms. They were spied on day and night by the guards, and not allowed to move more than ten feet from their hovel. Campbell was not tortured again, but as a result of his ill-treatment he suffered from acute headaches and severe pains in his chest. At least his anxiety over his wife was relieved when he heard on 2 December of her safe delivery.

Both men were constantly frustrated in their attempts to complain to the Rajah, or even get a message through to Darjeeling. All communications had to pass through their jailer, 'a truly odious being' according to Hooker, who wrote in a letter home:

> He is made up of malevolence and falsehood, the practice
> of which is his main occupation. He is a most filthy,
> squinting wretch: and he drives away everyone who comes
> near us, and causes our poor coolies to be flogged, when
> they approach the door, to beg a little food from our
> slender stock.

Hooker and Campbell nicknamed their jailer 'Evil Eye', the Dewan they called 'Butcher', and the Rajah 'Prince'. In this way they could safely discuss them in front of their captors without being understood. Despite their grim situation they managed to remain reasonably cheerful, and as time passed they developed a fairly warm relationship with the thugs who held them captive.

One of their most constant companions at this time, and one for whom they developed a great affection, was a little girl they named Dolly, who was detailed to supply them with firewood. She was ragged and dirty, but very quick-witted and kind, and a talented mimic. She loved to listen to Hooker whistling popular tunes, and made him a present of a Tibetan jew's harp, with which, when he was not smoking coarse tobacco in a brass Tibetan pipe, he whiled away the long evenings. Campbell delighted Dolly by playing an old harmonica, and his performances never failed to draw an audience of guards and local tribespeople.

Unknown to them, news of their capture had reached Darjeeling, and was causing a considerable dilemma. Both the military and diplomatic experts feared that if there were an attempt at a military rescue, the two men might be taken deeper into the mountains, and certainly their lives would be at risk. There was really little else to do but sabre-rattle from a distance. Troops and heavy artillery were moved up to the border in order to break the nerve of both the Rajah and the Dewan. The ploy succeeded, and Hooker and Campbell were taken under heavy guard to the border. Even on the way they feared they might still be murdered so that they would be prevented from giving evidence against their captors, and when a messenger sent from Darjeeling was violently sick after eating, Hooker, suspecting that their food was being poisoned, insisted that a hunting dog should eat the vomit. Eventually they reached Darjeeling safely, and shortly after their release troops moved in to strip the Rajah and Dewan of their power and wealth, and part of Sikkim was annexed to the British Crown.

Joseph Hooker returned to England on 25 March 1851.

Despite all the dangers and difficulties, his expedition had been an enormous success. Strong rhododendron plants were already growing at Kew from the seeds he had sent home, and before long they were distributed throughout the country. To this day, in gardens throughout Britain, fine Sikkim rhododendrons that came from his seeds are flourishing.

Hooker's return from the East did not mark the end of his botanical collecting: he also worked in North Africa and America. In 1865 he succeeded his father, Sir William Hooker, as Director of Kew Gardens. Sir William had pursued, with great effect, the plan for Kew laid down by Sir Joseph Banks, which was to make it the greatest collection of plants in the civilized world, an international reservoir of seeds and plants, and a centre for the development of botany as a science. Joseph Hooker, who was also to be knighted for his services to botany, carried the plan through to its completion.

GEORGE FORREST
(1873-1932)

George Forrest was always irresistibly attracted to wild places where he could wander freely and observe nature. He was born at Falkirk in Scotland on 13 March 1873, and every spare moment of his childhood and early youth was spent in the hills and on the moors near his home in Kilmarnock, fishing, bird-watching, collecting butterflies and observing the plants. His great love of natural history was fostered by his brother, a keen amateur naturalist. After leaving school, Forrest first worked in a chemist's shop where he handled the dried plants used in herbal cures and picked up a smattering of medical knowledge, and this was to serve him well in the years of exploration which lay ahead of him. Life behind a chemist's counter soon palled, however, and when he was left a small legacy he used it to travel in 1891 to Australia to visit relatives. Excited by the pioneer spirit of the country, he worked in the goldfields and spent some time on a sheep station. In 1902 he returned home, after a brief stop in South Africa, and took up life very much as he had left it.

He could well have gone back to a quiet, uneventful existence in Kilmarnock but for a chance discovery, which had nothing to do with plants. One day, while fishing on Gladhouse Loch in Tweedsdale, he was caught in a sudden shower and sought shelter under an overhanging bank. As he sat waiting for the rain to pass he spotted the corner of an ancient stone coffin sticking out of the soil, and through a crack he could see that it contained a skeleton. His curiosity aroused, he went to the antiquarian museum in Queens Street, Edinburgh, to learn more about his discovery. He must have impressed the academics there, because his visit to the museum led to a meeting with Professor Bayley Balfour, Regius Keeper of the Royal Botanic Gardens in Edinburgh, who gave him a job in the herbarium, sorting, listing and cataloguing the preserved plant material which daily arrived from plant collectors and botanists.

For a man who liked the open air and exercise it was probably dull work, but it was, perhaps, the most valuable training Forrest could have received for his future career as a plant collector, which he was already planning. To keep fit, he walked the six miles to and from work, refused to use a stool but stood all day at his bench, and spent his weekends tramping the countryside, fishing and shooting. His taste was for the solitary life: he loathed cities with their crowds and cluttered streets and pavements, and always dressed as a countryman in heavy tweeds.

In 1903, when he was thirty, he was introduced to the great horticulturist Arthur Kilpin Bulley, a cotton-broker who devoted a great deal of his fortune to sponsoring plant collecting, largely for his own garden. When Bulley offered him the chance to go to China as a collector, Forrest needed no second bidding. With scarcely any practical experience of collecting plants and seeds, and absolutely no knowledge of the Chinese language and its many perplexing dialects, he set off. Within a reasonably short time he was not only a fluent Chinese speaker but had trained a team of coolies to collect for him, a system which meant that, although he worked alone, through his native collectors he was able to cover a very wide territory.

Bulley sent him to explore the high plateau and mountain ranges of north-west Yunnan and south-east Tibet, where he was to collect the seeds of new and rare alpines. The area was dominated by three great rivers – the Yangtze, the Salween and the Mekong – all of which rose in the huge frozen highlands of north Central Tibet, and flowed almost side by side through the mountains before fanning out, the Mekong emptying into the China Sea near Saigon, the Salween into the Bay of Bengal, and the Yangtze into the Gulf of Tongking. It was, said Forrest, 'a marvellous country, planned on nature's grandest scale, prodigal in flora and fauna, rich in minerals'. Nearly all the tribes were of Tibetan origin, 'the diversity of whose customs, languages, and religions is truly remarkable. Like the slopes of the Caucasus, the region might be called the country of the hundred nations.'

Between Tengyueh (now Tengchung) and Talifu two hundred miles away, the rolling plateau rose to 11,000 feet, and was slashed by the deep valleys of the Salween and Mekong, and their many tributaries. The tops of the ridges were covered by dense forests of pine and hardwood trees, which thinned out to smaller shrubs such as *Rhododendron vialy*, *R. formosum* and *R. fortunei*. Clambering among the trees and shrubs were *Clematis armandii* with its saucer-shaped white flowers, and *C. fasciculiflora*, *C. nutans* and various forms of *C. montana*. In dry sunpockets Forrest found *Clematis chrysocoma* with its soft rose-coloured flowers and golden, glistening foliage, and considered none more beautiful. He also described *Clematis forrestii* :

> This is a scandent shrub of twenty to thirty feet in height. The foliage is finely cut and ornamental, the flowers pendulous on long pedicles in axillary clusters from five to six. Each is nearly an inch in diameter, the perianth a soft and creamy yellow, with anthers and filaments a brilliant shade of rose magenta.

For a plant hunter it was a paradise. On the hillsides he found a mass of shrubs – rubus, dipelta, viburnum, spiraea, philadelphus, deutzia, styrax, illicium, ligustrum, berberis, coriaria, buddleia, benthamia, kerria, camellia, magnolia and hydrangea. The grassland, especially where it was damp and boggy, abounded with herbaceous plants such as anemones, primulas, gentians, corydalis, pedicularias, spiraeas, senecios, potentillas and asters. On the high limestone ridges of the Shweli-Salween Divide between Tengyueh and Tali he found some of the finest rhododendron species – *Rhododendron souliei, R. sulfureum, R. crassum, R. bullatum, R. trichocladum, R. neriiflorum, R. campylogynum* and *R. lacteum var. macrophyllum.* In the same area, growing in open situations, he found what must be one of the finest garden shrubs, *Pieris forrestii,* with its handsome foliage and beautiful scented lily-of-the-valley-like blooms. And in the shady gorges and on the moss-covered boulders he found a wealth of terrestrial orchids such as *Pleione delavayia,* with its purplish-rose flowers marked with deep crimson, *Pleione grandiflora* whose snow-white blooms were blotched with crimson lake, and the orange-yellow and brown *Pleione forrestii.* He revelled in the wonderful primulas, and found *Primula malacoides* growing to perfection; but the most beautiful of all, he thought, was *Primula spicata :*

> None can compare with this species, the azure blue flowers forming a wonderful contrast to the silvery farina with which the plant is coated. The scapes are so slender that they seem scarce able to bear the weight of the relatively large flowers, which the slightest current of air sends trembling and swaying much in the manner of some of the campanulas.

Everywhere he travelled there were the most marvellous rhododendrons to be found. On the flanks of the range above the pine belt there was rhododendron forest composed of dense thickets growing as much as forty feet high. There he found *Rhododendron taliense, R. ficolacteum, R. anthosphearum, R. beesianum, R. rubiginosum, R. irroratum,* and the true *R. lacteum,* carrying massive trusses of canary-yellow blooms. Higher still were the dwarf species. Various forms of *Rhododendron intricatum* formed a carpet of purple, while the foliage filled the air with a spicy fragrance. As if this were not enough, the profusion of other plants included four glorious lilies – *Lilium thomsonianum, L. giganteum, L. delavayi* and *L. ochraceum.*

The weather in the area was also rich in variety. There could be brilliant, burning sunshine, dense fogs, teeming rain, and sudden, terrifying storms. A curious feature of the Mekong

Valley was that almost every day at dawn, mist rose out of it in columns and formed great clouds. The clouds, which seemed to materialize out of nothing, actually arose because a vacuum which formed in the valley during the day was filled after sunset by cold, moist air sweeping down from the snow-capped mountains, and this layer of air, warmed by the first dawn rays of the sun, would be drawn back up in columns of vapour into the atmosphere, where it would condense into clouds.

It was these columns of mist that were to help save Forrest's life in July 1905, when he was collecting in the north-west corner of Yunnan. He was based at the French Catholic Mission Station at Tzekou, which was situated at 5000 feet on the banks of the Mekong river at the point in Yunnan where China, India and Tibet meet. This area of vast mountain ranges, great rivers, and numerous narrow valleys broken by cross-ridges and spurs is isolated from the rest of the world for half the year by snow. The rivers, which seem to squeeze through gorges, are quite unnavigable. At that time the Upper Mekong could only be crossed by flimsy-looking bridges constructed of split bamboo, 'across which people are slung trussed up with leather thongs like chickens ready for the spit'.

This area was in 1905 in a considerable state of unrest. The lamas were up in arms, largely as a result of the clumsy and ill-considered invasion of the Holy City of Lhasa by Colonel Younghusband's expedition against Tibet. Tucked away in the mountains, the lamas of the Yellow Sect lived in huge lamaseries and, through a mixture of superstition and force, lived off the peasants, quite ignoring the Chinese who tried to control the area. The lamas were furious not only about the British attack on Lhasa, but also over an attempt by the Chinese to establish themselves at Patang (Paan), a strategically important town on the main highway from Szechuan to Lhasa. The Patang lamas had risen in revolt and murdered a high-ranking Chinese official and all his followers in Patang in March 1904. They also massacred the French missionaries stationed in the town, and their converts.

The uprising spread south to Atuntze, the Chinese-Tibetan

trading station on the east bank of the Mekong, and in April
Chinese officials and troops were sent in to the town (now known
as Tehtsin) to restore order; but they handled the situation
ineptly and were trapped there. Every day brought new and
more frightening rumours about the revolt and the atrocities
being commited by the lamas against missionaries and Christian
converts. Even though the lamas were hostile to them, the
French missionary priests had long been established in their
mission at Tzekou: their leader, Father Dubernard, had arrived
in China when Napoleon 111 was at the height of his power.

Despite the growing problems, Forrest and his troop of well-
trained and faithful Lissoo porters continued collecting, and
managed to assemble nearly 1000 herbarium specimens, a large
quantity of seeds and bulbs, and also a fine portfolio of photographs of plants growing in the wild. But the situation rapidly deteriorated, and even the Tibetans who had been friendly deserted
them. It was impossible for Forrest and two old priests to
defend the Mission against large numbers of heavily armed
lamas, so the news that Atuntze had fallen produced a mixture of
terror, confusion and despair; the native converts knew that if
they fell into the hands of the lamas they faced a long and
terrible death by torture.

There was nothing left for them but flight, so on the night of
19 July 1905, by the light of the rising moon, they all set off
along the narrow, treacherous track by the Mekong towards the
village of Yetche thirty miles away, where they knew there
was a friendly chief and some Chinese soldiers. The party
consisted of the two old priests riding mules, the native Christ-
ians, and Forrest and his porters, about eighty people in all.
The track ran below the walls of the lamaserie of Patang, and
as they passed by it one of the party made a noise. It was enough;
a whistle shrilled out, warning the roving bands of lamas of
the escape, and the party raced through the shadowy moonscape
with a kind of helpless urgency, praying they would reach
Yetche ahead of the soot-blackened lama warriors.

Early in the morning they reached a village, only to be told
that a forced march had taken the lamas ahead of them, cutting

them off. 'The local headman, a drunken and treacherous rascal, found many excuses to delay our flight, and thus we lost more valuable time', Forest recalled when he described the adventure in the *Gardener's Chronicle* in 1910.

By midday they had climbed well above the river and had a clear view of the countryside. To the north there rose a great column of smoke over Tzekou, where the Mission had been set on fire, so they knew there was no going back. It was obvious that the lamas were on their trail, and Forrest urged the party to press forward as fast and for as long as they could, in the hope of breaking out before the cordon was closed around them. However, the two priests, seeing the destruction of what had been their home for so many years, lost heart, and were now convinced they were going to die. They insisted on stopping by the side of a stream to prepare themselves for death, along with their converts.

For Forrest, brought up in a solid Scottish Presbyterian tradition, the sight of the two old priests holding a Mass to prepare their souls and the souls of the faithful for death at the hands of the lamas, instead of trying to effect an escape, was infuriating. He climbed up a nearby spur of rock, and had hardly reached the summit when he saw a large number of armed men running at full speed along the route they had just covered.

His warning shout brought complete panic, and the party scattered in all directions. Père Bourdonnec, one of the priests, blind with terror, crossed the stream by a fallen tree and plunged into the forest, despite attempts to stop him. He had run barely two hundred yards when he was riddled with poisoned arrows, and as he collapsed the Tibetans fell on him and hacked him to pieces with their great double-headed swords. One by one, the the other members of the party suffered a similar fate. Ten of the women committed suicide in the river rather than fall into the hands of the lamas, and only fourteen of the native converts escaped. Of Forrest's party of seventeen collectors and servants, only one survived.

With everyone either dead, captured or scattered, Forrest knew that there was nothing to do but run. The valley they were in was about four miles long and one and a half miles wide. The west side was sealed by a high ridge of rugged hills, north and south were cut off by the lamas and their Tibetan supporters, while to the east was the Mekong. Forrest started to run flat out towards the Mekong down a precipitous track, which was in places little more than a shelf made of logs and planks along the face of a sheer cliff. Rounding one of the sharpest bends, he came face to face with a band of heavily armed Tibetans, who immediately gave chase. For a moment he considered trying to shoot his way through them with his repeating Winchester and heavy revolver, but realizing the shots would bring even more of the enemy, he turned and raced back up the path. Once out of sight, he leapt off the path and plunged into the forest below, and rolled and tumbled two hundred feet before being stopped by a large boulder. Bruised, cut and scratched, his clothes torn to shreds, he lay gasping for breath, expecting any minute to be discovered and hacked to death. But the Tibetans, assuming that he had continued up the valley, ran past him.

Forrest did not dare move until nightfall, when he decided to try to break out to the south. Painfully he climbed three thousand feet over rocks and through dense jungle, only to find that a cordon of watch-fires and savage Tibetan mastiffs blocked his escape. Wearily he returned to his hiding place by the boulder.

For a week, moving at night and hiding by day, he tried to find a way out of the net, without success. In almost total despair, he came to believe that his only hope was to make a stand and shoot his way to freedom, despite the fact that he was hopelessly outnumbered. At least, he thought, he would have the satisfaction of taking a large number of lamas with him before he was killed. An opportunity arose while he was lying in the scrub beside a stream. He spotted a band of warriors searching for him, and was just about to bring down the first when, higher up on the hillside, he saw the unmistakable figure of Father Dubarnard gesturing to him to make his way downstream. He obeyed the priest and so gave his pursuers the slip.

The hunt was relentless, and he recalled that he 'was kept

continually on the move, trapped and hunted like a wild beast by the lamas and their Tibetan adherents, who thirsted for my blood'. He had to bury his boots in the bed of a stream, because they left such distinctive tracks. He had to wade shoulder deep in the icy water to avoid capture. On one occasion he thought he was finished when he ran into a group of Tibetans, and two poisoned arrows passed through his hat as he fled. Another time, his hiding place was discovered by Tibetan women who had been sent to track him.

There was no time, day or night, that he could relax. He was sleeping behind a log in the bed of a stream when he was woken by a party of thirty lamas in full war array, making a crossing a few yards away. He wrote that, 'Armed as I was I could have shot down most of them, but, though enraged as I was at the time I held myself in check, as I knew that to fire one shot would bring a hornets' nest about me. My only chance was to keep still.'

At the end of eight days he no longer cared whether he lived or died. His feet were hideously swollen, his hands and face were ripped and cut by thorns, he was caked with mud from head to foot, and he was weakened by starvation. On the morning of the ninth day he became delirious, and when lucidity returned he knew he must make one final bid for freedom. In the valley there were two hamlets inhabited by Lissoos, a sub-tribe of the Tibetans. He decided to hold up one and force the people to give him food.

On the evening of the ninth day he limped into one of the hamlets with his gun cocked and trained on the startled inhabitants. Filthy, unshaven, his clothes in rags, and his face, hands and feet scabby with mud and blood, he must have presented a terrifying figure, but luck was with him. The people were friendly and offered to take him in and hide him, which was an act of courage as well as charity since they must have known that if they were caught sheltering a foreigner they would be killed.

The only food they had was tsaniba, a coarse meal made from ground wheat and barley, but Forrest fell on it as though it was the finest French cuisine. Eating so ravenously after days of starvation – he had only eaten a few grains of corn and some peas which he had found – caused inflammation of the stomach, from which he was to suffer for some months.

For four days the Lissoos hid Forrest while they made arrangements to smuggle him to safety. First he was taken by guides down to the Mekong to another friendly village, where they were informed that a band of Tibetans searching for the collector had spent the previous night there. He and his guides kept themselves hidden until sunset, when local hunters took them to a remote farmhouse a few miles away. Here he stayed until guides arrived to take him through the mountains to the Chinese-Tibetan town of Hsias Wei Hsi.

The journey through the mountains was appalling. It was the middle of the rainy season, and the escape party had to travel in the worst downpour Yunnan had known for generations. Forrest's enthusiasm for plants nevertheless remained undiminished. He wrote: 'Up and up we climbed, cutting our way through miles of rhododendrons, tramping over alps literally clothed with primulas, gentians, saxifrages, lilies etc., for these unknown hillsides are a veritable botanists' paradise.'

At about 18,000 feet they reached the snowfields. They had no covering at night, and had to survive on a few mouthfuls of parched barley; and because the sleet and rain fell in such a deluge it was impossible to kindle a fire. When they reached the summit they turned south. For six days the route was across glaciers, snow and ice, and sharp, jagged limestone outcrops which tore and cut Forrest's feet. Once they felt they were safely out of range of the lamas, they turned east down the mountainside, back to the Mekong, hacking their way through dense bamboo thickets.

Forrest was in pain and exhausted, but his suffering was not at an end. As they were approaching a village at about 9000 feet, he stepped on a 'panji' buried to protect a maize field from raiders. The fire-hardened, sharpened bamboo spike pierced his foot, protruding at least two inches. For days he was in agony, and it took months for the wound to heal.

Eventually the small party reached the right bank of the

Mekong, opposite Yetche, the village Forrest had hoped to reach with the Mission party. At considerable personal risk the headman, a friend of his, crossed the river to bring him clothes and fresh food – pork, chickens, eggs and cakes.

Despite the long journey over the mountains, he was still not out of danger. The area was full of lamas, so he continued down the right bank disguised as a Tibetan, until he was opposite Hsias Wei Hsi. Here an attack was expected at any hour, but some of the townspeople came to his aid and he was hauled across the river on a rope bridge. In the town he ran into Père Monbeig, a missionary who had managed to escape from the lamas. Forrest's first enquiry was about Father Dubarnard, whom he had last seen on the hillside above the valley. He learned that not only was the old priest dead, but that he had been cruelly executed some days *before* he had seen him urging him down the stream. For two days the priest had hidden in a cave before being run to earth. The lamas dragged him to the burnt-out Mission of Tzekou, where he was horribly tortured and mutilated, then killed. Had Forrest been saved by a ghost?

A few days after his arrival at Hsias Wei Hsi, Forrest left for the safety of Talifu, where there was a small Chinese garrison, with an escort of two hundred Chinese soldiers. During the time he was trying to escape from the valley, he had been reported as dead to the Foreign Office. Fortunately the news had been withheld from his family until just before he arrived in Talifu, but they grieved for a week before hearing of his survival.

Apart from his rifle, revolver and two belts of cartridges, he had lost everything – camping equipment, stores, photographs and collecting equipment. But the real blow was the loss of a whole season's work:

> A collection of most valuable plants numbering fully two thousand species, seeds of eighty species, and one hundred photographic negatives. It is difficult to estimate the value of such a loss; coming from an entirely un-explored area, probably one of the richest in the world, there was undoubtedly a very large percentage of new species.

He had sent pieces of specimens home in letters to be examined by botanists, and a dozen, about a third of all he sent back, were found to be new to science and to horticulture.

With the disappointment of the loss, and the sheer horror of his experience, Forrest might have been expected to return home, if only to restore his health, but he never even entertained the idea. All he wanted to do was to get back into the field. On 11 October 1905 he set off to explore the Upper Salween river with his friend George Letablère Litton, Acting British Consul at Tengyueh. Their trip was dogged by local wars and feuds, and the people living in the villages they passed through told them many tales of bloody battles. They saw for themselves mouldering corpses and skeletons beside the tracks (although the deaths could have been caused by disease as much as by fighting). Close by a wretched hamlet they spotted some freshly dug graves in a field, and were told by the villagers that they contained the bodies of the headman and two others who had been killed by men from a village further up the hills, and that their village had retaliated with a raid which left eight of the enemy dead. A few days later they went into another ramshackle village where the only inhabitants were a few women and children. All the adult males had been wiped out by raids and famine.

Sometimes their own progress was hampered by being caught in the middle of a feud. One day they were attempting to cross the Salween by rope bridge to a large village called Lo-ma-di. After an uncomfortable night on the opposite bank, they met a man from the village who volunteered to fetch the ropes and runners necessary to haul the thirty-five men and a dog in the explorer's party across the river. While they were waiting, a party of people from the village on their side of the river approached them. They were wild-looking, aggressive and threatening, because there was a feud between the two villages over who should operate the bridge and collect tolls from travellers. Forrest's party offered to give an equal present to both parties but 'when our friends from the left bank returned with the runners, we saw at once we were in for a serious disturbance', he wrote.

The leader of the right bank party shouted to the left bankers that they must not help the travellers across and, to reinforce his point, shot a poisoned arrow into the river. The next one that he fitted to his bowstring was clearly intended to find a human target. The situation was now extremely dangerous, and ready to explode into violence and bloodshed. Forrest, recalling his next move, wrote: 'Mr Litton and I at once rushed at him, and I fired several shots from my Winchester repeater over his head at a boulder on the other side of the river. The effects of seeing the bullets smash against the stone at such a distance was immediate.'

So as not to lose the advantage, Forrest and Litton told the man and his companions through their interpreter that if they drew another arrow the next bullet would be fired at them. 'They at once subsided into an awe-struck silence', Forrest recorded, but even so he and Litton had to put up a constant display of marksmanship to keep them under control.

The country they were passing through was largely unexplored by Europeans, and the tribespeople were quite unfamiliar with white men. Litton's job was to make contact with headmen and establish diplomatic links, and while he was involved in long negotiations with the headmen and their advisers, Forrest was free to botanize.

Their journey took them in and out of different botanical zones. On high alpine slopes Forrest found vivid patchwork scrub of spiraea, philadelphus, deutzia, berberis, buddleia, camellia, magnolia and, of course, the usual wealth of rhododendrons. In damp hollows and grassy places there were primulas, gentians, potentillas, asters and anemones. Such was the extreme character of the terrain he was exploring that in the deep river valleys, with their humid conditions, he was rewarded with orchids, particularly pleiones, whose lavish blooms ranged from deep crimson to rich yellow, handsomely marked with splashes of brown.

While the plant and insect life was rich, birds and animals were conspicuous by their absence. Writing about this remote and rewarding region in the *Royal Geographical Society Journal*, Forrest observed:

. . . the river banks at a low altitude, and where wholly sheltered from the north winds, have an almost tropical climate, and vegetable and insect life is both vigorous and troublesome. Creatures with inconveniently long legs plunge suddenly into one's soup; great caterpillars in splendid but poisonous uniforms of long and gaily coloured hairs arrive in one's blankets with the business-like air of a guest who means to stay. Ladybirds and other specimens of Coleoptera drop off the jungle down one's neck, while other undesirables insert themselves under one's nether garments. The light in the tent attracts a perfect army of creatures which creep, buzz, fly, crawl and sting. Scissor insects make the day hideous with their strident call, and the proximity of the Lissoo coolies introduces other strangers, of which *Pulex irritans* [the human flea] is by far the least noxious.

He went on to describe the difficulties of walking over much of the terrain, where the paths were narrow tracks, 'choked with the luxuriant growth of the previous rains, slippery and lop-sided'. In some places they had to haul themselves over boulders by means of hanging branches, or scramble along the cliff-faces using notches in the rocks, 'more suitable for monkeys, Lissoos, or other creatures gifted with more prehensile feet than a European'. The vegetation, in fact, seemed even more of a problem than the insects:

Poisonous looking scarlet fruit hang from the overarching jungle; lianas and tree-roots trip up the unwary traveller; if he catches the nearest plant to save himself, the chances are that it is a stinging nettle of the size of a laurel, and poisonous in proportion. In some places, especially around maize-fields, the natives provide a further diversion in the shape of a 'panji', or hard pieces of sharp-pointed bamboo, which are driven into the grass, and will, if trodden upon, pierce even through a leather boot and deep into the foot. It is only when the traveller, scratched, bruised, and with torn clothes, emerges on a quiet sandbank by the river, or onto some open terrace high above it, and finds the camp fire lighted, the tents pitched, and a pailful of hot water ready for a bath, that he begins to think that exploring the Salwin [sic] is a game worth the candle.

Despite his cheerful grumbling, Forrest was captivated by the country of the Upper Salween. He said it could never be forgotten

> by anyone who has wondered at it in the rich sunshine which prevails after the autumn rains have given way to the first touch of winter. The great variety of rock formation, the abundant forests and vegetation, and the diversity of light effects between the summits of the ranges (at 10,000 to 13,000 feet) and the abyss in which the river flows produce a vast panorama of ever-changing beauty. In the morning the sun, as it touches the top of the Mekong Divide, sends wide shafts of turquoise light down the side gullies to the river, which seems to be transformed into silver. The pines along the top of the ridges stand out as if limned by the hand of a Japanese artist. In the evening all the wide slopes of the Mekong side are flooded with red and orange lights, which defy photography and would be the despair of a Turner. The traveller whose fortune it has been to explore the great rivers of this our north-east Indian frontier will admit that the Salwin [sic], while it is inhospitable, difficult, and barbarous far exceeds in natural beauty all the valleys of the sister rivers, the Yang-tze, the Mekong, or the Irawadi [sic].

It was surprising that Forrest could write so lovingly of an area where, only a few months earlier, he had been hunted like a wild animal by people whose sole ambition was his capture and death by slow torture. That he should agree to accompany Litton in a territory whose valleys must have seethed with the most frightful shadows of death was quite extraordinary. But danger and fear were secondary to the overpowering attraction the wilderness held for him. Such was his compulsion to collect that when, in 1906, he suffered a serious attack of fever, he made arrangements with his collectors to continue working before he travelled to Talifu to receive treatment at the China Inland Mission.

In 1912 he set out on his third expedition. China was again in a state of uproar. When he reached Tengyeuh from Talifu in the middle of May, the city was in appalling chaos. Since the autumn of 1911 it had been in the hands of revolutionary troops led by a former coolie, Li-Kin-Yen. The soldiers were completely undisciplined, and more interested in loot than ideology. On the orders of Yen the general commanding the Tengyeuh troops when the revolution broke out was murdered, along with his officers. Forrest wrote:

> This creature then took command and turned the place into a perfect shambles. Squeezing and beheading was the order of the day, and is still, though to a lesser degree. In all fully two hundred and fifty have been beheaded . . . and all without the slightest vestige of a trial.

The ordinary people of the city, who had originally supported the uprising, were treated abominably, and wanted to see the old order restored. Forrest recorded:

> It is difficult to say what even a month may bring forth. Living in China just now is like camping alongside an active volcano. Yungcheng-fu [Paoshan], about five days on the Tali road from here, has been burned out by the rebels and a very large number of people killed or executed.

The situation was further complicated by the fact that the rebels had issued a republican dollar made more of tin than silver, and called in all the block silver, the universally accepted form of currency. Because the merchants were therefore understandably reluctant to cash his cheques, and because of rapid inflation, Forrest had the greatest difficulty in buying the essential supplies he needed for a long expedition. Those who did take his cheques charged an exorbitant commission.

Despite the difficulties, he was able to get out into the hills and valleys and gather a fine collection of plants and seeds before conditions became impossibly dangerous, after the commander of the Chinese troops stationed in the area beheaded ten lamas in their lamasery and brought the entire Tibetan population to arms. At this point Forrest left Tengyeuh for Burma, trekking through rugged country with thirty coolies, all opium addicts, and with his baggage and collections packed on the backs of a dozen mules.

Eventually Yunnan became calm again, and he was able to go back there. On his return he had his first sight of *Rhododendron sinogrande*. He noted that it seemed to be 'a magnificent species. The capsules are two to two and a half inches long, slightly curved and as thick as one's thumb. The foliage runs from one foot, six inches to as much as two feet by ten inches, dark green and glossy on the upper surface, ash colour beneath; very handsome tree of twenty or thirty feet'. His judgement was right: the shrub was to receive an Award of Merit from the Royal Horticultural Society in 1922, and a First Class Certificate in 1926.

The strain of trying to organize and carry through expeditions against the background of political and civil turmoil that was tearing China apart eventually took its toll. In 1913 he complained of feeling ill, which was unusual for this broadly built man who rarely mentioned illness or discomfort. Whatever he was suffering from soon passed, however, and he was able to note:

> I am quite all right again, as hard as whipcord, but a bit weary at times with all the hustle. I never seem to get a rest or even an hour to myself. Every minute is fully occupied. My day is from 6.30 a.m., to 11 or more p.m., with scratched half hours for meals. However, there is a good time coming. I keep looking ahead.

In 1914 he undertook a particularly arduous journey through beautiful but very rough country. The route was along a main road that was little more than a goat-track, and almost washed away by days of violent thunderstorms and heavy rain. The Yangtze Valley at Fengkow was fiercely hot, and the country so barren it was almost a desert. Forrest's party spent a night and most of the following day camping on a sandbank where the rocks were too hot to touch, and the temperature was 110°F in the shade. 'I simply lay, gasped and drank muddy Yangtze water', he recalled. But his efforts were repaid when he discovered a double white form of *Rosa banksia*, which grew there to perfection.

In the mountains, away from the hot river valleys and gorges, he often imagined himself at home on his Scottish moors:

> Take the moors and hills surrounding the headwaters of any of our principal Highland streams in the early spring, in full flood, with patches of snow around. For heather and heath imagine mile upon mile of dwarf rhododendrons at that season almost the exact brownish shade of dried heather, and you have the scenery of the summit of the Bei-ma-shan [which lies between the Mekong and the Yangtze in the Tehtsin] at fifteen thousand feet. The raw damp wind strengthened the impression for me, and, as I stood there my heart warmed to it and I could almost imagine myself at home.

In 1930 Forrest decided to make one final expedition before retiring. Its purpose was to tie up all the loose ends of his lifetime's work in Yunnan, and to fill in the gaps formed by the plants he had missed on previous forays, or those that needed reintroducing. He organized and controlled his collectors from his base in Tengyueh. The project went splendidly, and exuberantly he wrote home in a letter:

> Of seeds such an abundance, that I scarce know where to commence, nearly everything I wished for and that means a lot. Primulas in profusion, seed of some of them as much as three to five pounds, the same with meconopsis, nomocharis, lilium, as well as bulbs of the latter. When all are dealt with and packed I expect to have nearly if not more than two mule loads of clean seed, representing some four to five hundred species, and a mule load means one hundred and thirty pounds to one hundred and fifty pounds. That is something like three hundred pounds of seed. If all goes well I shall have made a rather glorious and satisfactory finish to all my years of labour.

It was a glorious finish, but sadly he did not live to see his final collections safely back in England. On 5 January 1932, as he walked out on the hills a few miles from Tengyueh to shoot game, he suffered a massive heart attack within sight of his camp and was dead before he struck the ground. The tough, determined Scot had finally worn himself out.

He was buried in a small graveyard at Tengyueh, next to his friend Consul Litton, who had died twenty-six years earlier of fever. The legacy Forrest left to gardeners was enormous: it included hundreds of species of rhododendrons, and also conifers, acers, berberis, buddleias, camellias, daphnes, deutzias and cotoneasters, as well as a wealth of primulas, lilies, alliums, anemones, irises and asters. The list goes on and on, with gems for every part of the garden, from shrubberies and herbaceous borders to rock gardens.

ERNEST HENRY WILSON
(1876-1930)

Many of the most beautiful plants and animals live in the most inaccessible parts of the globe. Perhaps this is just as well, since it is quite certain that if they did not, many of them, if not eaten or exploited, would by now be destroyed or so reduced in numbers as to be on the verge of extinction. The careless destruction of plant species began with mankind's first need for fuel and building materials, and land clearance for food production, but has been hastened by the more recent growth of populations, industry and the discovery of minerals.

Among the many men and women who recognized the danger to plant life throughout the world was Augustine Henry, a British Customs Service officer working in China, both in Ichang, a town on the Yangtze, and Szemao in Yunnan. A talented amateur botanist, he devoted the greater part of his spare time to collecting, mainly for the Royal Botanic Gardens at Kew. Increasingly worried by the massive destruction of forests in his area for the manufacture of charcoal, for it was quite evident to him that the loss of the trees and shrubs would lead to the decline and disappearance of large numbers of different plant species, he appealed to Kew to send a trained botanist to make a definitive collection. The man they sent was Ernest Henry Wilson. Born at Chipping Campden in Gloucestershire, Wilson had left school when little more than a boy and become the general assistant at a nursery garden in Solihull, from which he graduated to the Birmingham Botanic Gardens. Clever and ambitious, he attended classes at the Birmingham Technical College where he won the Queen's Prize for Botany, and this academic success led him to Kew.

Kew could not raise the money to finance an expedition, so it had worked out an agreement with Veitch and Sons, then the greatest nursery gardeners in Britain, and possibly in Europe. Veitch wanted to introduce more hardy plants to an expanding market which reflected a growing enthusiasm for laying out great natural gardens and assembling impressive collections of plants. There was at this time a move away from formal garden designs, with their vast regiments of bedding plants, towards landscaping and planting that took their lead from nature. What Veitch needed was a Kew-trained man with a keen eye for a good garden plant, and Wilson fitted the bill exactly.

Henry's expeditions had shown that there were many fine garden plants waiting to be collected, and that the area was unique in having species which were the key to the geographical distribution of plants, certainly throughout the Asian landmass, and probably over great tracts of the world. Wilson's main commission was to find and collect seeds of what appeared to be a unique tree which Henry had spotted. He had been unable to collect any seed, but the beauty of the plant haunted him, and his description excited the House of Veitch. The tree was *Davidia involucrata,* first recorded by the missionary-botanist Father Armand David, and since then known by a variety of names – the pocket-handkerchief tree, the ghost tree and the dove tree. Its flowers are relatively insignificant but they are surrounded by a large triangular white bract, and in full bloom present an unforgettable sight. As well as searching for the tree, Wilson was to gather herbarium material for Kew, and also seeds, bulbs and plants.

Wilson arrived in China in 1899 and made his way to Yunnan where he had a rendezvous with Henry, who gave him directions to the davidia he had seen growing in a remote valley. Armed with Henry's instructions, Wilson set off on an arduous journey, but the map was good and he reached the valley without difficulty. There was no doubt that it was the right spot, but there was no sign of the tree. Eventually he found some tribesmen and was able to make them understand what he was looking for. They pointed to the stump of a felled tree and then to a ramshackle hut built from its timber. His sense of failure and frustration was painful, as it must have been for so many plant collectors who, having discovered a fine plant, returned to it when the seed was ripe only to find it to have been eaten by a passing goat, cut for fodder, or simply burnt for land clearance.

Fortunately, Wilson was not the kind of person to accept defeat, and since he knew that if there was one plant there must be more, he continued to search. Eventually he was rewarded with a grove of davidias all splendidly displaying their handkerchiefs, and from which he was eventually able to collect seed.

Wilson's first trip did not only teach him the virtue of patience, but also revealed to him the dangerous character of the country which was his collecting ground. At the turn of the century the borders of China and Tibet were hazardous and unpredictable. Small revolutions and uprisings broke out with little warning, as war-lords and would-be war-lords struggled for power. There was always the chance that a plant hunter could spend a whole season collecting, only to see everything destroyed, or to be forced to abandon all in a flight for life. On his way to the meeting with Henry he had been seized on suspicion of being a spy and held in the town of Lao Lai, a stinking, over-crowded place (now Laokai in North Vietnam) where he spent his time nursing other Europeans who were daily dying from fever. When he did finally get away from Lao Lai his enterprise nearly ended in disaster when his boatman, an opium addict, almost caused them to be wrecked on rocks in the Red river.

Wilson remained with Veitch for about five years, during which time he established himself as a major collector, bringing to English gardens treasures such as *Clematis montana rubens, Clematis armandii,* the graceful *Acer griseum* with its vivid autumn colouring, the beauty bush, *Kolkwitzia amabilis,* which

Robert Fortune (above) greatly enriched gardens
with the plants he collected during his arduous
years in China. One of the loveliest and most
popular of his finds is *Deutzia scabra* (below), and
he also discovered the winter-flowering jasmine,
Japanese anemones and the shrubby winter-
flowering honeysuckle, *Lonicera fragrantissima*.

The 'Stream of Nine Windings', its twisting
course threading its way through fantastic rocks
and peaks, was in just the kind of Chinese
landscape that enchanted Robert Fortune, in spite
of the fact that it held many dangers.

Dwarfed by the lush extravagance of the rain
forest, Richard Spruce, photographed beneath the
arching fronds of the mumbaca palm, *Astrocaryum
mumbaca*, was quite at ease in the green wilderness
of the Amazon where he spent fourteen years.

The camp at La Veta Pass, Colorado (top),
which Joseph Hooker (seated left) shared with the
American botanist Dr Asa Gray (seated
foreground), was luxurious in comparison with the
conditions under which he worked in the
Himalayas in 1848, when he found and collected
the magnificent Sikkim rhododendrons.
They included *Rhododendron falconeri* (above), with
its huge trusses of creamy-yellow bell-shaped
flowers, richly marked with purple blotches.

Although he often had to face enormous dangers,
George Forrest (top, with his dog and his
collectors) always gave the impression of being a
man out for a pleasant hike, as he trekked to and
fro among the Himalayan ranges. One of the most
successful and prolific of plant hunters, Forrest
trained native helpers to harvest seeds so that
a wide area could be covered. His unerring eye
gave gardeners such treasures as the scarlet-flowered
Rhododendron nerriiflorum (above).

Ernest Henry Wilson (left, above) is immortalized
in gardens throughout the world by *Lilium regale*,
the regal lily, the collection of which nearly cost
him his life, but one of his favourite plants was
what he called his 'Beauty Bush', *Kolkwitzia
amabilis* (left, below). Like Wilson, Reginald
Farrer (top) developed an early passion for plants,
and as a boy he hunted in the hills of Yorkshire
for alpines. After expeditions to the Pyrenees he
travelled to the Himalayas, where he and his
companion William Purdom found such superb
flowers as *Clematis macropetala* (above).

Frank Kingdon-Ward was a tireless explorer and
plant collector, and made many fine discoveries. He
found the giant Himalayan cowslip, *Primula
florindae* (above, left) and also made the first
discovery of a nomocharis in Assam, *Nomocharis
aperta* (above right), a striking satiny pink flower.
Joseph Rock (below) enjoyed the role of grand
traveller. He often dressed as a Mandarin,
insisted on his dinner being served with style in
even the most wild places, and he once had a
personal caravan which stretched for half a mile
over the mountain roads of China.

he regarded as one of his most outstanding introductions, and the glowing yellow poppy-like *Meconopsis integrifolia*. It was unfortunate that he did not become a Veitch collector earlier, for the great nursery was in decline, and although his finds at first grew well there, they were in the end neglected, and consequently many of them failed to reach the market.

In 1906 Wilson established firm links with the Arnold Arboretum in Boston, USA, part of Harvard University, links which were to last for the rest of his life. On his way to China for the first time, he had spent a short time at the Arboretum, and become a close friend and admirer of the Director, Charles Sprague Sargent. The regard was mutual, and when Wilson was free, Sargent had no hesitation in appointing him to collect in the plant-rich territory of the Chinese-Tibetan border for the botanic garden.

Whenever possible, Wilson used the great rivers that cut their way through the Chinese-Tibetan Alps to travel to within trekking distance of the remote valleys and mountainsides which held the floral riches he sought. The rivers were treacherous and dangerous, but they speeded up the process of travel, which was otherwise painfully slow because the only other way was along narrow mountain tracks and through dense forest with matted undergrowth. Frequently a track would peter out at a sheer cliff-face which would have to be scaled before one could rejoin the path, which then continued across the mountain like a broken seam.

To assist travellers, the mountain people constructed crude perpendicular ladders which were lashed to the rock faces, but they were slippery and not always in the best state of repair. To ascend or descend them required strength, nerve and an excellent head for heights. Both people and animals were unnerved by them: on one occasion Wilson had to blindfold his dog to carry him down one of these ladders, and even then the poor creature clawed and struggled so much that both he and his master were nearly pitched into the abyss.

The main river used by Wilson was the Min, a tiny flood compared with the mighty trinity of the Salween, Mekong and

Yangtze rivers, but rising like them in the forbidding fastness of Tibet, and, in fact, a tributary of the Yangtze. It was in a valley of the Min that he first spotted *Lilium regale*, the white regal lily. Even among the brilliantly coloured and enticingly named hybrid lilies, and other exquisite species of lilium, it stands alone, and is certainly among the ten best garden plants in the world. It is the most generous of plants – easy to grow, beautiful to look at, and sweetly scented. In their classic work, *Lilies of the World*, Hubert B. Drysdale Woodcock and William Thomas Stearn state that Wilson first introduced the lily through Veitch, having discovered the plant in 1903. It was then incorrectly identified as *Lilium myriophyllum*, and came into cultivation in 1905. It was not recognized as a new species until 1912, which perhaps explains the curious fact that it took some time to earn popularity. But, said Woodcock and Stearn, writing in 1950, 'to this find of Wilson we are indebted in great measure for the present revival of interest in lily culture, since it is as easy to grow as it is lovely to behold'.

Lilium regale was collected at the expense of acute suffering and a sickeningly close brush with death. Its lack of success irked Wilson: he knew it was a fine and special plant, but it was making little impact in Britain, and he had completely failed to introduce it to America. He could not forget the sight of vast numbers of the lily in full flower, crowded into narrow valleys in the far west of Szechuan, and filling the air with their wonderful, heady scent. In 1910 he decided to go back and collect enough bulbs and seed to ensure that his lily would flourish in gardens throughout the world, even in countries that could not boast a single native lily. Recalling this expedition in his book *Plant Hunting*, Wilson wrote:

> My quest was the Regal Lily which I had discovered some years earlier but had failed successfully to reintroduce into American gardens. Its beauty of blossom and richness of fragrance had won my heart and I was determined that it should grace the gardens of the western world. That such a rare jewel should have its home in so remote and arid a region of the world seemed like a joke

130

on nature's part. However, there it was, and my business
in life was to effect its transference to lands where its
beauty would find proper recognition.

Throughout the indefinite past, generations of the
Regal Lily have lived unsung and unseen save by the rude
peasants of a rude land. But few white men had passed
that way when first I made my discovery and none had
noted my royal lady. This had been preserved for me.

He left Boston in March, on a journey remarkable for its tortu-
ous roundabout route. First he made for Europe, where he eventually joined the great trans-Siberian railway on the long trip to
Peking, and from there he made for the garrison town of
Sungpan in Tibet, and thence to Shanghai. The regal lily
was certainly tucked away: from Shanghai it was necessary to
travel 1800 miles up the Yangtze river to join the Min, which he
then had to follow for a further 250 miles into Tibet, pushing
deep into a harsh mountainous country sparsely populated by
tribespeople, 'a land where Lamaism, Buddhism and Pallism
strive for mastery of men's souls; to a region where mighty
empires meet'.

It was there, in bare, harsh valleys surrounded by snow-
capped mountains, that the lily grew. In summer the valleys
were burning hot, and in winter locked in by bitter cold, and
without warning terrible gales would scream through the
narrow clefts in the mountains. But in June the valleys were
transformed, and Wilson wrote of them:

> . . . by the wayside, in rock-crevice by the torrent's edge
> and high up on the mountainside and precipice this lily
> in full bloom greets the weary wayfarer. Not in twos and
> threes but in hundreds, in thousands, aye, in tens of
> thousands. Its slender stems, each from two to four feet
> tall, flexible and tense as steel, overtop the coarse grasses
> and scrub and are crowned with one to several large
> funnel-shaped flowers, each more or less wine-coloured
> without, pure white and lustrous on the face, clear
> canary-yellow within the tube and each stamen filament
> tipped with a golden anther. The air in the cool of the

morning and in the evening is laden with delicious
perfume exhaled from every blossom. For a brief season
this lily transforms a lonely, semi-desert region into a
veritable fairyland.

Anyone who has grown *Lilium regale* will know that Wilson's
description is not an exaggeration. Its scent, mingling with
that of honeysuckle and roses on a summer's evening, is one of
the crowning experiences of the gardening year.

Wilson made his base at Sungpang Ting (now Sungpan)
which was close to the sweeping grasslands of that part of Tibet.
The Chinese who then occupied it used it as a clearing house for
trade with Tibet, and herbal medicines and musk were brought
in by the natives for barter with the Chinese merchants. For a
few days he rested there, checking his baggage and making
certain that nothing had been overlooked. Then he and about
twenty porters and collectors set off for the march through the
gorge cut by the River Min, a seven-day journey. On either side
of them, great mountains towered out of sight into the clouds.
There were few houses, but terraces and almost flat pieces of land
were cultivated. The heat was searing, and often there was little
shade on the narrow tracks which had been hacked out of the
rock. In some places the road-makers had had to blast tunnels
through the mountains, and at regular intervals grave warnings
in giant Chinese characters were carved on the cliff-face, alerting
travellers to the danger of landslides and rock-falls. This
hazardous track was the main road between Sungpan and the
large towns and cities of Szechuan, and it was busy with gangs
of coolies and mule-trains carrying brick-tea and cotton cloth,
medicines, hides and deer-horns. For two groups travelling in
opposite directions the pass was particularly dangerous.

Since he was an important man in China, ranking at least at
mandarin level, Wilson had to take a sedan-chair with him as the
mark of his position and respectability. It was a simple structure
of rattan cane which Wilson used as rarely as decorum would
allow, preferring to walk with the coolies and mules, ever watch-
ful for plants. The chair was more important than a passport,
for it earned the respect of the people.

By the seventh day the party was some 6000 feet above sea-level, and surrounded by grim, inhospitable near-desert country. But it was only the valleys and immediate mountain-sides that were so barren: high above them was forest, and even small villages and farmsteads. Through the valleys a fierce, unrelenting wind howled almost constantly, so strong that it was difficult to walk against; but although the leaves of maize were ripped and torn by the wind, the regal lily survived.

It was in these uncomfortable surroundings that in October 1910 Wilson made camp and set his collectors to work. They dug seven thousand of the lily bulbs out of the stony soil, a harvest which would certainly ensure that his 'royal lady' would take her proper place in the garden-plant hierarchy.

With the bulbs packed and loaded, they set out for Chengtu Fu, the capital of Szechuan. Four months of constant travelling were beginning to tell on Wilson, who for some days had been suffering from a mild form of dysentery. Unusually for him, he took to his sedan-chair, but his ill-health was a small thing, quite overshadowed by the pleasure and satisfaction of knowing that he had found and collected *Lilium regale*.

His chair led the caravan, and was followed by a man carrying his bulky plate camera and tripod. Ahead of them all, as usual, was his black spaniel dog. The party gave scant attention to the dire warnings carved into the rock of the dangers of the road, since they had already travelled so far without halt or accident. Wilson was at ease with the world; the weather was endurable, the lurching movement of his sedan-chair was almost soothing and, above all, his precious lily was packed up and secure.

Suddenly his dog, whose wagging tail had reflected the mood of the party, froze, whined and then rushed forward as a small piece of rock rattled down the mountainside, hit the road and bounced off into the river that raged through the gorge three hundred feet below them. Wilson yelled out a warning. High above them he could hear the rumble of a landslip growing to a roar. His bearers put down his chair and ran for cover, while he scrambled out to follow, only just getting clear before a huge boulder struck the chair, sweeping it into space, down to the

river. He ran towards an overhanging rock, ducking instinc-
tively when a fist-sized boulder whistled through the air,
taking his sunhat with it. He hoped he was running clear of the
fall, but before he could reach the shelter of the rock he was
suddenly thrown to the ground, and simultaneously felt as
though a red-hot wire had passed through his right leg. He
tried to jump up, but found that his leg was useless, and he had to
crawl to the safety of the rock. Rocks crashed and splintered like
shrapnel on the track, and clattered to the river far below. From
somewhere beyond his refuge came the moans of the man who
had been carrying his camera and tripod; his skull had been laid
bare by a flying rock.

The pain in Wilson's leg was growing worse; his tough pig-
skin puttee had been sliced through as if by a sharp knife and
forced round his leg, the toe cap of his boot had been torn off
and with it the nail of his big toe, the side of his calf was deeply
cut, and the leg itself broken in two places beneath the knee.
Fortunately, he remained conscious. Had he not, it was likely
he would have been abandoned by his panic-stricken men, and
unless help had come along there was every chance he would
have died on the exposed mountainside.

Two of his men had taken shelter under the same overhanging
rock, and soon they were joined by others from the party. Nearly
fainting from the pain, Wilson ordered them to fetch his camera
tripod and told them how to convert it into a splint. The landslide had spent itself, so his men moved him out onto the track
where they bound the splint to his shattered leg. While this was
being done a mule train came lumbering towards them, and
since the track was too narrow for them to turn back, and their
drovers did not dare to stop in case the slip started again, there
was nothing for it but for Wilson to lie still and let the animals
step over him. He later wrote:

> How many people know the size of a mule's hoof?
> Quite a number have felt the strength of a mule's leg and
> the sharpness of his teeth; his obstinacy is proverb. But
> the size of his hoof is another matter. Frankly, I do not

know with mathematical exactness but as I lay on the
ground and more than forty of these animals stepped over
my prostrate form the hoof seemed enormous, blotting
out my view of the heavens.

Although their hooves seemed the size of dinner plates as they
were lifted over him, the mules stepped with such care that
not one hoof so much as brushed his clothes.

Fortunately, since his chief servant also rated a sedan-chair,
and his had escaped undamaged, Wilson could be carried in it.
He was lifted into it and his mangled leg lashed to one of the
carrying poles. Because of the severity of his injuries and the lack
of proper treatment they could be given, there was a real danger
of infection and gangrene, so it was decided to make a forced
march to Chengtu. Every movement of the chair, however
carefully the coolies carried it, caused Wilson excruciating
agony, but as long as there was daylight to see they marched flat
out, and in three days reached their destination.

At Chengtu he was taken to a doctor at the Friends' Presbyterian mission. His filthy, bloodstained clothes were cut away and
the bones set, but despite the doctor's skill they refused to mend
and infection set in. Other doctors living in the city were
consulted, and they concluded that his life could only be saved
by amputation. Such an operation would have ended his career
as a collector, and he refused to let the doctors go ahead. 'Some
cutting and slitting was done and the infection stayed', he
recalled. After three months he could hobble about on crutches,
but he knew that if he were to save his leg he must get back
to America. So he hired a boat and set off on a journey which
took him right across China, from the borders of Tibet to the
East China Sea, via Ichang, where he took passage on a steamer
for Shanghai, stopping for medical treatment at the missions
they passed.

Eventually he arrived in Boston, where he was taken to hospital. The infection was cured, but because of it the leg could not be
put in a cast and the bones had to be left to grow together as
well as they could. This left his right leg shorter than the left,
and with a limp he called his 'lily limp'. But the handicap did

not prevent him continuing to travel widely throughout the world in search of new plants; and neither did his accident result in the loss of a single regal lily bulb.

Wilson did not return to China, but because it was from that country that he had made his greatest introductions, he earned himself the nickname 'Chinese Wilson', a name which was neatly immortalized in that given to the lovely climbing white cluster rose he introduced, *Rosa sinowilsonii*. His Chinese introductions are to be found in almost every garden – *Jasminum primulinum*, now known as *J. mesnyi*, the primrose jasmine, and roses, berberis, ribes, paeonies, rhododendrons, primulas, lilies, aconites and poppies. He introduced well over 1000 species, as if he found plant collecting effortless.

The Arnold Arboretum became his home, and in 1919 he became Assistant Director. Eight years later, following the death of Professor Sargent, he was appointed Keeper. Despite his administrative position, however, he continued to travel. He visited Formosa and Korea, always collecting and always with a clear eye for a good garden plant, and so catholic was his taste in plants that his travels also took him to Australia, Tasmania, New Zealand, India, Singapore, Japan, Penang, Kenya, Zimbabwe, and South and East Africa.

It was in Japan that he made another major horticultural discovery which must rate in importance with his regal lily: he found the evergreen Kurume azaleas. He was utterly bewitched at his first sight of the neat, beautifully grown plants in a Japanese nursery garden, multi-hued and brilliant as a patchwork quilt. He described the flowers as 'the roguish eyes of laughing, dimpled, and blushing blossoms'. For centuries the Japanese had been intensely jealous of their plants and most reluctant to allow any to be taken out of the country, which perhaps explained why the Kurume azaleas had to wait until 1920 to be introduced to Western gardens. It also says much for Wilson's tact and diplomacy that he was able to obtain a collection of named plants, which have become known as 'Wilson's fifty'. Of those original introductions, nurserymen still stock varieties such as Azuma-kagami, Hinodegiri, Iro-hayama, Kirin and Kure-no-yuki, ensuring that his 'divine Princess Kurume' lives on to reign in garden borders along with the regal lily.

Although the greatest part of his life's work was in America, he never lost his love for England, and returned regularly. He planned to retire to his home county of Gloucestershire, but this was not to be. On 15 October 1930, when he was driving home with his wife after visiting one of their children, his car went into a skid, smashed through a fence and plunged down a steep embankment. His wife was killed instantly, and he was dead on arrival at hospital. There is a kind of ghastly irony in the fact that this man who, in his own words, 'lived in Nature's boundless halls', had escaped death by drowning, starvation and crushing, only to be killed by a modern motorcar on a modern highway.

REGINALD FARRER
(1880-1920)

Among the scratched, bruised, battered, footsore company of plant hunters, Reginald Farrer is the odd man out. Although a superb gardener, he was not trained in nursery or botanic gardens. Instead, his knowledge of botany and growing plants was acquired in a more leisurely fashion, against the protective background of wealth and privilege, unlike so many of his number who learned their trade the hard way.

Born at Ingleborough in the west of Yorkshire, he was disfigured from birth by a hare-lip which had to be corrected by a series of operations. He was thus regarded as a delicate child and educated at home, and this protected him from the brutality of Victorian public school life. He was left alone from an early age, to develop his love of plants and gardens, and his writings, though they show a tendency to be carried away by explosive hyperbole, reveal a love for plants that went very deep. He spent much of his time in the hills around Ingleborough which were unusually rich in native alpines, and from which he made an extensive collection of dried plants. At the age of fourteen he had a short article describing *Arenaria gothica,* which he had found growing at Ingleborough, accepted by the *Journal of Botany*.

At the same time he began building a rock garden at his home. He disliked intensely the then fashionable mounds of broken stone and the sludgy green waste from glassworks which were used to construct rockeries; in his view they looked more like the rubble from a building site than the alps they were supposed to represent in miniature. The Victorians were also fond of using white quartz, to simulate the eternal snows, but Farrer preferred the local limestone for its more natural effect. At Oxford (where he took a second in Mods and a third in Greats) he made friends with a don and together they designed and built a rock garden, by the side of the lawn at St John's.

After Oxford he travelled widely in the European mountain ranges, gathering alpines and learning his trade as a plant collector. In 1903, at the age of twenty-three, he visited Japan, and in 1907 went to what is now Sri Lanka, where he became a Buddhist. His conversion was not some exotic whim but a deeply held conviction, although he did not try to convert anyone to his new religion. The depths of his belief are revealed in a letter to a friend written in 1920 when he was travelling in Upper Burma, after a visit to Mandalay, where he had handled a relic of the Buddha. He wrote:

> I had a shattering experience just before I left, which you will appreciate. For I not only saw, but actually had in my hands, the oval crystal reliquary in which fragments from the pyre of the Wholly Perfect One Himself had lain inviolate in the ruins of the vast golden Pagoda in which Kaniskha the Emperor enshrined them nearly 2000 years ago, in a Greek wrought casket of bronze, that was never touched again until, in 1910, the ruins of the Dagoba were discovered and explored. The unutterably Holy Thing revealed lying, as it had always lain, in its secret chamber. All the feelings about relics may be mere sentimental snobbery, but it does give you strange feelings to have between your own fingers that gold-bound little drum of crystal, sealed at both ends, and to see inside the little papery kafuffle of whiteness and ash, that actually, in its time, was part of the mortal Epiphany of Gautama Buddha.

In 1911 he attempted to enter politics, standing unsuccessfully as the Liberal candidate for Ashford. Clearly his heart was not in it; he spent much of the money given him by his father to further his political career on buying cypripedium orchids; and it is in fact a mystery that he ever believed for a moment that he could have made a career for himself in the claustrophobic atmosphere of Parliament, when his one true love was the airy freedom of high mountain ranges.

Before long he had exhausted the European Alps, and turned his eyes to the east and the rugged Tibetan-Chinese Marches. A meeting with the plant collector William Purdom transformed this idea into reality, and in 1914 they travelled together, by way of the Trans-Siberian Railway, to Peking, and finally to the Kansu-Tibet Border.

It would have been hard to have chosen two more dissimilar people to share the hazards of a plant-hunting expedition in such an inhospitable region. Purdom was a tall, athletic figure, withdrawn but quietly charming, while Farrer was stocky, tending to plumpness, dark haired, with a heavy moustache covering the operation scars on his lip. He had a harsh, grating voice, and, when he chose, a deliberately rude manner; genuine expressions of affection towards friends could be wiped out by merciless sarcasm. Purdom had started life as a garden boy and graduated to Kew, while Farrer had always had his own gardeners to carry out his horticultural grand designs. But the two men had one thing in common – a passion for flowers and mountains.

Farrer had chosen this wild, rugged region of Kansu because he argued that plants from so far north would be hardier than those gathered in Yunnan, which was in any case an area already being thoroughly collected. As he and Purdom made their way across the vastness of Russia and China, Farrer dreamed of filling English gardens with marvellous new plants; what he did not foresee was the state of turmoil that would greet him when he reached his destination.

The whole of the Kansu-Tibet border was in a state of chaos, due to a revolution led by a terrorist known simply as the White Wolf. It was never clear whether the White Wolf was a single war-lord or half a dozen bandits, but the answer was merely academic: the very name was enough to strike terror into the population, as the atrocities committed in his name were horrible. A favourite display (later adopted by the Communists in dealing with landlords) was to tie the victim to a table, carry him into the village square and slowly chop him into small pieces. Not surprisingly, the people sought safety in those towns with a garrison of Chinese soldiers. When Farrer and Purdom arrived they had the greatest difficulty in recruiting porters and hiring mules. The porters were afraid to risk their lives, and the mule owners were not prepared to risk losing their animals.

Eventually they did get together an expedition, and made for the mountains. In order to cover a greater area they split up, and while Farrer seemed to avoid most of the trouble, Purdom was less fortunate. He and his party of porters ran into a band of 200 brigands, who shot dead two of his horses before he could shoot his way to freedom and to Farrer, who was then in the house they were using as a base. The porters were so thoroughly scared by this that during the night they ran away, having cut a hole through the flimsy wall of the building.

In addition to this, the lamas of the region turned against them. Farrer got off to a bad start with the holy men by riding his pony along a forbidden path, which resulted in the two 'foreign devils' being held responsible for a violent storm that wrecked the peasants' crops. In consequence of this, the prior of a powerful lamasery at Chagola plotted their murder, and it was Purdom who found himself facing a mob of tribesmen with arquebuses on their weapon rests and burning fuses in their hands. Farrer, in his rather florid style, recorded Purdom's reaction:

> Armed only, then, with his fascinating smile, and hands thrown wide to show his harmlessness, he braced himself to face those smoking guns and that howling mob . . . the villagers gnashed and bellowed upon him as he came, with faces and gestures so devilish that it was long before they deserted his dream.

The situation deteriorated to such a degree that the plant hunters were forced to retreat across the border into China.

The combination of the White Wolf, lamas and the outbreak

of the First World War brought the expedition to an early close, but despite the difficulties Farrer brought home a wonderful collection of plants, many of which earned the coveted Royal Horticultural Society Awards of Merit and have now become familiar garden plants. They included *Buddleia alternifolia, Deutzia albida, Viburnum fragrans, Potentilla fruticosa, Clematis tangutica* and *C. macropetala, Gentiana farreri, Lilium centifolium* and *L. duchartrei var. farreri.*

He returned home to a wartime desk job with the Ministry of Information, but his mind was still in the mountains. His Kansu experiences enabled him to add considerably to his great work, *The English Rock Garden,* and he also wrote two books about his travels, *The Rainbow Bridge* and *On the Eaves of the World.*

While his contemporaries collecting in the mountains of the East were professionals, Farrer was very definitely an amateur, which was both his strength and his weakness. He hunted plants with the eye of an artist, seeking beauty above all else. Pure botany meant little to him, and as a result his herbarium collections were the despair of the scientists. He was impulsive, scorned forward planning, and seemed to live a charmed life in dangerous country where not only the terrain presented enormous dangers, but bandits or religious zealots were also a major problem.

Just after the war, when Farrer was in a nursing home recovering from an operation, he met Euan Cox, who was to become his friend, travelling companion and biographer. In his book, *Farrer's Last Journey,* Cox recalled:

> I remember the occasion of our decision so well. The War was just over . . . I climbed innumerable stairs and interrupted a tea-party where Armistice politics were being discussed. The guests left, and Farrer exclaimed that the hills were empty and the times seemed propitious. Somebody suggested – I have forgotten which of us – that we should join forces. Our trip was settled in five minutes, and in another fifteen we had decided on somewhere in Upper Burma.

In six weeks they were kitted out and had 'bolted from England on the first available steamer, only too thankful to be off to some country where there were high hills sufficiently unexplored'.

The two men spent a happy year in Upper Burma, with Cox 'content to sit at the feet of the master'. So great was the impression made on him by Farrer that, eleven years after Farrer's death, he was able to write this account:

> I have a vivid memory of Farrer in the hills, his stocky figure clad in khaki shorts and shirt, tieless and collarless, a faded topee on his head, old boots, and stockings that gradually slipped down and clung about his ankles as the day wore on. The hustle of the early start; the constant use of the field-glasses which always hung around his neck; the discussions, very one-sided owing to my ignorance, about the value and relationship of the various plants; his intense satisfaction when a plant was once in the collecting tin and was found worthy; his grunt of disapproval when it was worthless; the luncheon interval with its attendant cold goat rissole and slab chocolate; his enjoyment of our evening tot of rum, a necessity in the rains; and, above all, his indomitable energy that never spared a frame which was hardly built for long days of searching and climbing. All these, I say, are as fresh to me as if they had happened yesterday.

Farrer was totally absorbed when he was botanizing, with eyes only for plants, and he would often trip and stumble because he never looked where he was putting his feet, and his ankles and legs would be scratched by thorns and slashed by sabre-sharp bamboo stumps. Cox remarked that 'his legs usually looked like a ploughed field; but he cared little. He plastered them with grease, and otherwise left them to look after themselves'. When he was travelling between collecting grounds, through botanically dull country, he would drift off into a kind of trance. An ungainly horseman, he would roll to the wallowing gait of his rough mountain pony, whispering to himself, 'and', wrote Cox, 'his lips would move for hours on end, while he imagined conversations or concocted themes'.

They began their expedition at the town of Myitkyina on the banks of the Irrawaddy, a huddle of bungalows, tin huts, barracks, a court-house and a club. Here they assembled a party of twenty-four mules, five muleteers, two orderlies, two grooms, two servants and an assortment of hangers-on, before heading out to Hpimaw and the Chimili valley.

The route lay for part of the way beside the N'mai river, a dangerous water-course that the local tribesfolk believed to be the home of evil spirits and, as Cox observed, it was unpredictable:

> Most terrifying of all are the pools. For a second or two they are glassy; then tiny circles appear that in turn give place to concave caps which finally disappear with a swish and a gurgle; and the surface becomes glassy again. No one can play pranks with the N'mai.

After crossing the Chipwi Hka and a small ridge of hills, they plunged into the valley of the Ngawchang where they found their first rhododendrons, a fine clove-scented, white-bloomed plant similar to *Rhododendron ciliicaly,* and another with deep salmon-pink flowers.

The country was exceptionally beautiful, but life was hard for the tribes of this remote corner of Burma. When one of Farrer's servants shot a sambur, an elk-like creature, the entire neighbouring village turned out for a share in the feast. Cox recalled:

> The onlookers held aloft blazing torches, which glinted on rows of gleaming faces and greedy eyes; then torch after torch spluttered, and the light faded until in the dusk the circle looked like a row of vultures, while bits of meat were shoved into the embers and then eaten singed and half raw. It was hours before the grunting and commotion died away in the silence of repletion.

The valleys were humid and fecund, and the trees were smothered with orchids, ferns, mosses, lichens and creepers; and the closer they drew to Hpimaw the more common were the rhododendrons, the ivory white of *R. araiophyllum,* crimson *R. tanastylum,* and the wonderful deep crimson trusses of *R. heptamerum.* But the magnolias were the real glory of the forest. Cox became ecstatic over *Magnolia rostrata :*

> In a gully sweeping down to the valley was tree after tree of a Magnolia in full bloom – and such a Magnolia. Not a leaf-bud had burst, but every branch was laden with great upstanding cups of a marvellous variety of colour ranging from purest white through the softest of pinks to a rich salmon and rose flushed with the purple tints seen in the staining of the petals of *M. soulangiana.*

The same day they found *Primula sonchifolia,* with its luscious foliage and its orange-eyed vivid blue flowers, and rejoiced to find themselves in the midst of such a floral treasure-house.

The arrival of five of George Forrest's collectors from Tengyueh on the Chinese side, to collect along the frontier, jolted Farrer out of his state of bliss. He was furious, regarding the intrusion as nothing short of trespass on his territory. Botanizing was forgotten while he spent the remainder of the day firing off complaints to Forrest by letter and telegraph. His fury was totally misplaced, since Forrest's men were collecting only on the Chinese side of the range, and had merely taken a day off to see what Hpimaw was like.

Dwarf bamboo was another source of annoyance and discomfort. It grew everywhere, even invading the smallest cracks and crannies. Cox complained:

> It plagued us in every way. It soaked us, it stabbed our legs whenever it was cut; it caught our clothing at every step. If we stood on a cut stem our feet would slide out from under us, when we would clutch the stems by the pathside and get an involuntary showerbath in a wild effort to keep ourselves from falling.

But they had to cope with the bamboo in order to gather the lovely plants that grew among the thickets. One treasure was *Rhododendron oemulorum,* which thrust itself out of the densely packed stems to a height of sixteen feet, with beautifully felted leaves and deep scarlet flowers.

The marvellous plants they discovered were set in an extraordinary landscape. One day when they were sitting on a rock and eating their lunch, with China in front of them and Burma behind, the thin silver snake of the Salween river could be seen far below them, and beyond that the Mekong-Salween divide. There the waxy scarlet flowers of *R. phoenicodum* blazed amongst the green, and from every tree hung great sprays of the gorgeous white orchid *Coelogyne cristata*, with its bold orange flash in the centre of its lip.

From Hpimaw they trekked into the Chimili valley, where they were plagued by clouds of particularly virulent midges, but the valley was the source of some fine rhododendrons, especially *R. aiolosalpinx*, which had a colour range from pure white to deep rose, and the peach-coloured *R. caloxanthum*. Among the grass and rocks they found primulas and, less welcome, ticks. Cox found that one the size of a small crab had attached itself to his chest.

In June 1919 the rains came, and thunderstorms battered them. They were making their way to Hpimaw after hearing that it had been burned to the ground, and on the journey there, the terraced bank of a river gave way under them, and they were hurled into the water in an avalanche of liquid mud, and had to be rescued by their coolies. But the weather soon changed, and the countryside was once more alive with flowers. One of the finest was *Nomocharis pardanthina*, which grew in its thousands on the hillsides. Writing in the *Gardener's Chronicle* of 1 November 1919, Farrer declared:

> . . . when you see it on the open, high alpine grass-slope below Hpimaw Pass, nodding down at you with myriads of wide-open, dark-eyed faces, in every shade of pale rose and every degree of freckling, there is nothing very much left for you to look at on the Hpimaw Pass.

With the flower season at its height, a quicker means of transport than their legs was needed, and Bhaju, their chief servant and aide, was despatched to find a horse. He produced a skinny, eccentric pony which they bought for one hundred rupees, and named Ma. It turned out to have a vast appetite and a disconcerting habit of falling asleep every few hundred yards. Determined to miss nothing in the Chimili valley, Farrer and Cox established a camp there, in an idyllic glade where a stream burst out of a gap in the rocks, and they slept on soft mattresses of dwarf rhododendrons. Primulas and saxifrages carpeted the turf and boulders, and, as Cox said, 'We could not move a step without trampling on something that we would have given a fortune to transport bodily to our gardens'.

The abundance of plants was overwhelming, but to reach them involved exhausting marches in and out of valleys and up and down steep mountainsides. Nevertheless, whenever they stepped out onto an alpine meadow all bruises and aches and pains were forgotten, in what Farrer described as

> . . . the full glory of the open meadow . . . one simultaneous riot of colour, laid on, not in dottings and pepperings, but in the broadest and most massive sweeps such as might satisfy the most opulent day-dreams of a herbaceous borderer. The flowers blend by the acre, not by the dozen, or even by the hundred; there are solid furlongs of tender pink Geranium, yellow Globeflower, crimson Polygonum, citron Primula, violet Delphinium, golden Anemone, golden Saxifrage, golden, fragrant Corydalis, and a soft, pale-blue Lactuca like a softened *Cichorium intybus* with pendant flowers. The whole picture combines in such a vast unbroken blaze of colour that even from far away below, down in the camp, the hillside is seen to be painted all over with an indefinite luminosity which distance is unable to determine.

Normally when it rained they would keep at their search, sheltered by huge blue Chinese umbrellas, but when the weather 'came down in blatters of wind and rain', as Cox put it, they would retire to bed to read, or play piquet. It was, they concluded, an almost perfect life, doing 'just as you like without feeling the derangement that attacks the system if you are a creature of habit and insist on the day being plotted out in advance'. The plant hunt was followed by the harvest, and while they were gathering and drying seed in the Chimili valley they found a baby panda, which they adopted. This tiny ball of mahogany and black fluff was named Miss Georgiana Grunts and would perch on their sunhats 'like the eagle on a Kaiser's helmet'. Sadly, she developed a mysterious skin complaint and died.

With the harvest safely packed and freighted, the two men travelled to Mandalay, where they spent Christmas. Cox had to go to India on his way back to England, so they parted at Rangoon, and Farrer took a bungalow at Maymyo in the mountains above Mandalay. Here he stayed for a long rest, surrounded by a garden filled with roses, violets and sweet peas. He started work on a novel and planned a second journey to the north of Burma, 'away over the Back of Beyond, out across the last lone edge of Nowhere'. He was depressed to hear from Sir Isaac Bayley Balfour, Regius Keeper of the Royal Botanic Gardens in Edinburgh, that the live plants he had sent home had all arrived dead, and that the herbarium specimens were all muddled up and that many of the labels had gone astray. In fact a few plants did survive, and he was heartened to be told that his seeds were the best to have been received from the East.

After a few months at Maymyo he returned to Myitkyina, where he met up with his porters and servants and thirty-two mules, later increased to thirty-seven, and also the ridiculous horse Ma (who eventually ran off with some buffaloes and could not be caught). After a long, hard journey he reached the point where the Akhyang river and the N'mai meet, and climbed into a forest rich in rhododendrons.

In May 1920 he reached Nyitadi, which he found wonderful. He wrote to Cox:

> . . . it sits 2000 feet lower than Hpimaw: but at the junction of two torrents, with a semicircle of Alps around and glens radiating up into them. In the middle of the foreground is a sort of a little Luksang, dividing the streams; and, to the left of this, a very big, wild, jungled Luksang, acting as portal to a range of tremendous peaks, like frozen

flames of black granite, perfectly inaccessible and fantastic.

His bungalow was little more than a flimsy shack built of bamboo. It had no windows, but there were so many gaps that they were not necessary. The wind and the rain drove in, and the smoke from the fire in the middle of the building seemed reluctant to seep out. It was an unpromising place, but Farrer rigged up shelves and tables, arranged his books and stores along the walls and declared it 'a snuggery'.

Within a few days he had discovered two new rhododendrons, *R. chawchiense,* whose magenta flowers he regarded as repulsive, and a towering forty-foot tree, *R. hylosum,* which had large rose-coloured bells speckled with crimson. Much of his time here was spent in the Chawchi Pass, in the mountain range which separates Nyitadi from the Salween river. In July he camped at 12,000 feet and found an abundance of riches. 'The flora seems to get richer as you come north. The specimen book now gives 50 solid Rhodos, and of these 30, at least, unknown in 1919', he wrote to Cox. For a while he could find no primulas, the flowers he treasured above all others, but he eventually discovered a crimson one, and another with huge white bells. A large yellow meconopsis delighted him, as did a vermilion nomocharis.

His camp was, he said, 'perched on the wall-coping of the world with India, Burma, China, and Tibet all fluttering in my view'. The rain never quite stopped: if it was not falling in torrents, it mizzled. Books fell to pieces, and clothes, blankets and furniture were permanently sopping. It was cold and uncomfortable, but Farrer was happy, and wrote '. . . not only did I stick out my self-appointed time up there, but I even made it a real joy and happiness to do so. I painted flowers and I wrote and all was very pleasant. . .'

In August he climbed into the Moku-ji Pass. It was to be his last expedition. The area was not particularly abundant in new plants, but he did find two interesting hypericums as well as a daphne with apricot-coloured flowers, an elegant chestnut, and a magenta-rose-coloured marsh marigold.

He now found that he needed all his will-power not to surrender to depression in the constantly grey and dripping weather. 'I am being given every chance of becoming a saint or a sage if I don't incidentally become a corpse or a sponge in the process', he remarked, and, again in a letter to Cox, he said: 'I am surprising myself in a great many ways, but particularly in my unsuspected power of managing my nerves – turning them on and off like bath-taps, at different pressures, so as to continue happy.'

In his 'funny little Ritz of a shanty' he had no problem being cheerful, but when he was in the mountains that he loved so much he found that it required skill and determination:

> an unvarying life of sapping fogs does need the resolution of happiness pulling tight, and draw out one's reserves of serenity – to such an extent that, after four days of being down here again, I feel, as it were, my soul's banking account (I wish it were my other one) swelling sensibly, and vigour and joy pulsating back into my control reservoir, along all the veins of my spirit!

In the same letter from Nyitadi he mentioned a bout of fever from which he had suffered. He made it sound almost agreeable, 'a faint malaise, voluptuous stretchings and yawnings, fine delicious little thrills all over me', and one day later had recovered, after dosing himself with whisky and soda, and quinine.

At the beginning of September he was commenting on how well he felt, and how little he was affected by fatigue, but on 1 October he was suddenly taken ill with a severe cough and pains in his chest; twelve days later he was so ill he refused all food; and four days after this he was dead. The official diagnosis was diphtheria, which at that time was raging through the valleys, but it seems much more likely that he caught pneumonia as a consequence of weeks spent being soaked day in and day out. His heartbroken servants made a coffin and carried his body to the little village of Konglu, between the Irrawaddy and the Nmai Hka, and buried him high on a slope, among the mountains he loved so dearly.

FRANK KINGDON-WARD
(1885-1958)

Frank Kingdon-Ward was the last of the great professional plant collectors and, like his contemporaries Forrest, Wilson, Farrer and Rock, he chose Asia with its wealth of hardy plants for his hunting ground. For nearly fifty years he explored and searched in China, Tibet, Upper Assam and Burma, discovering scores of fine rhododendrons as well as a wonderful carmine cherry (*Prunus cerasoides rubea*); and he will always be remembered as the man who successfully brought the blue poppy (*Meconopsis betonicifolia baileyi*) to Britain, and found the last wild lilies.

Combining the qualities of an athlete with those of an intellectual, he was a man of outstanding ability and energy. He was born on 6 November 1885 in Manchester, where his father lectured in botany at Owen's College. Later the family moved to Cambridge when his father was appointed Professor of Botany at the University.

From a preparatory school, Frank Kingdon-Ward – the name Kingdon came from his mother's family – went to St Paul's School in London, from which he won a scholarship to Christ's College, Cambridge. The family was not well off, and when his father died in 1906 he had to leave Cambridge and find a job. Through the influence of an academic who was a close friend of the family, he was offered and accepted a post as a teacher at the Shanghai Public School, a British-run establishment in the Chinese trading port. This was to be his first step towards a plant-hunting career.

During the school holidays he travelled widely in the East, and in 1909, when he was offered a place with a zoological expedition which was planning to travel across China, he broke his contract with the school and turned his face towards the great wilderness of Asia. Although the expedition was concerned solely with collecting animals and birds, Kingdon-Ward, with his botanical background, made a small collection of plants, more for amusement than for any other reason. The notion of becoming a plant-hunter had not yet occurred to him; his mind was taken up with pure exploration.

On his return to Shanghai it looked very much as though, after all, he would have to settle for the more mundane task of earning a living and, had it not been for an upheaval in the horticultural world in Britain, this would no doubt have been his future. George Forrest had been principal collector for Bees Nurseries but in 1910 he was 'poached' by the great gardener and plantsman J. C. Williams, of Caerhays in Cornwall, so A. K. Bulley, Bee's founder, turned to Sir Isaac Bayley Balfour, one of the most distinguished Directors of the Edinburgh Botanic Gardens, who recommended Kingdon-Ward as a replacement for Forrest.

When the letter arrived in Shanghai asking him to collect hardy alpine plants in Yunnan and the Tibetan Marches, the reluctant schoolmaster needed no second bidding. Thus he began plant hunting, and during the years that followed he became a legendary figure among explorers. He survived disease and danger, overcame the most daunting difficulties, and introduced a treasury of plants into British, European and American gardens.

His first plant-hunting trip in 1911 did not start well. After a tedious trip to Burma, he made his way to the watershed of the Mekong river, where he became separated from his porters in the forest. He was soon lost; for hours he wandered among the densely growing trees and bamboo thickets. As it grew dark he stumbled over the body of a dead baby which had been abandoned in the wilderness. Night fell, the rain streamed down, and his only protection was a waterproof cape.

By morning the rain had turned to snow. He was chilled through and gripped by the despondent conviction that he would not be found, or find a way out of the oppressive growth that crowded about him. He stumbled on, sucking nectar from the rhododendron flowers that lit the gloom of the forest, and then eating the blooms, which caused agonizing stomach pains. He also shot a bird and ate it raw.

Growing weak and desperate, he came across an animal pen which he recognized, and from this ramshackle building was able to pick up the track that led him back to the village of Wei-hsi-t'ing, from where he had come. As darkness fell he had still not reached safety, and he began hallucinating, fancying that the trail was littered with great boulders, and that weird and threatening birds and animals stalked him. Eventually he did reach the little settlement nestling in the shelter of a valley, where, he discovered, a search party had been sent to look for him but had lost his trail and given him up for dead.

It was during this trip that he first saw blue poppies. At 16,000 feet on the Yunnan-Tibetan border he discovered a low-growing plant, with coarse prickly foliage, displaying the most beautiful scented blue flowers. He collected seed which later germinated, but even though the *Meconopsis* (poppywort) flourished in the wild close to the rim of a glacier, it failed to survive an English winter. He collected other blue poppy species but none of them did well in British gardens. Indeed, they were so unsuccessful that he grew tired of them and turned his attention to the more rewarding rhododendrons.

A true measure of courage is to be found in those who force themselves repeatedly to do something which terrifies them. Two great fears haunted Kingdon-Ward throughout his life, snakes and heights, both of which were to be found in abundance in his hunting grounds. The first, at least, were as wary of people as people of them, and Kingdon-Ward's encounters with them usually consisted of him running in one direction and a snake slithering off in the other. Heights, however, could not be avoided by anyone travelling in the great alps of Asia. Through-out his explorations he had to deal, often on a daily basis, with traverses which could be crossed only with the aid of hand- and toe-holds; and his route frequently lay along tracks chipped out of sheer mountainsides with drops of thousands of feet into river gorges, or across fragile rope-bridges swinging over furious torrents. During his third plant-hunting trip in 1914, he twice almost plunged to his death. His first fall over a precipice was halted by a tree, and the porters were able to haul him to safety, and on the second occasion he slipped off a path in the darkness, halting his plunge on a narrow ledge. When a torch was brought he found he was crouched on the edge of a sheer drop.

This trip was a nightmare of muscle-breaking climbs up into the mountains, down into the jungle and up again, of hazardous river crossings and blinding storms. One night when he was sleeping in a mountain village, a storm struck with terrifying force, 'as though someone was tipping barrels full of water and compressed air on top of us'. Through the deafening scream of the wind, Kingdon-Ward could hear the crash of his hut collapsing. He crawled out of the wreckage to see two other buildings totally demolished by the gale. Miraculously, no one was killed or injured.

When he finally marched out of the mountains and jungles and reached a frontier fort, he was greeted with the news that Britain had declared war against Germany. Now his only thought was to get to India and enlist, so he hurried to Fort Hertz (Putao) in Burma. This was a six-day slog down to the plains through undergrowth infested with leeches reaching out from the leaves, twigs and branches, to attach themselves to men or animals and feast on their victim's blood. Kingdon-Ward's dog, Maru, suffered horribly:

> I halted continuously to relieve him, on one occasion pull-ing six off his gums, two from each nostril, several from inside his eyelids, and others from his belly, neck, flanks, and from between his toes. Sometimes his white coat was red with blood. As for me, leeches entered literally every orifice except my mouth.

154

The scars left on his feet and ankles from the sores caused by the parasites remained with him for the rest of his life, and by the time he reached Fort Hertz he was in the grip of a raging fever so severe that his family was warned by telegram that his life was in danger. The medical staff at the fort nursed him back to health, however.

Kingdon-Ward joined the army in Rangoon, and for two years was confined to tedious administrative work, mainly as a censor, before being sent on more active service to Mesopotamia. In 1922 he returned to the Far East, exploring and plant collecting. It was a short expedition, which again ended in a bout of fever bad enough for him to be ordered back to England for medical treatment and a long rest. It was during this recuperation that he met and married Florinda Norman-Thompson, after whom he named the lovely *Primula florindae*. He also went into partnership in a nursery garden in Devon, but the venture did not flourish and was eventually abandoned. Neither did his marriage prosper. Although they had two daughters, after fourteen years they divorced, both declaring they would never remarry. (In fact, ten years later he did remarry.)

In 1924 Kingdon-Ward, accompanied by the Earl of Cawdor, a keen amateur naturalist, travelled to Tibet to explore the gorges of the Tsangpo river, which flows into the Brahmaputra, and to try to locate the fabled Falls of Brahmaputra. The expedition took the party through some of the most savage and least-visited country in the world, the great central plateau of Tibet. It was magnificent, but gaunt and cruel: day after day the plateau was swept by a relentless wind that whipped up an agonizing spray of sand, dust and gravel. Even at night, lodged in filthy hotels, they would face the discomfort of this dust, which would be compounded by attacks from fleas and lice.

Eventually they reached the junction of the Tsangpo and Gyanda rivers in the Assam Himalayas, and paused in their journey to recover before making the two-day march to the alpine meadows and rhododendron woods that surround the village of Tumbatse. Here, at a height of 12,000 feet, Kingdon-Ward's eye was caught by a flash of brilliant blue in the bushes.

At first he thought it must be a bird, but as he approached it did not move, and revealed itself as a poppy of the most vivid blue.

In 1913 Lt-Col. F. M. Bailey, who worked for the Indian Political Service, had been exploring the Brahmaputra river, and found a blue poppy in eastern Tibet. It was not in seed, but he noted its location and pressed a flowerhead between the pages of his pocket-book. This fragment was sent to the then Director of Kew Gardens, Sir David Prain, a leading expert on Himalayan poppies. Although he had little evidence to go on, Prain decided it was a new species, and named it *Meconopsis baileyi*. Bailey's poppy was remarkably similar to herbarium specimens collected by the Catholic missionary priest Père Jean-Marie Delavay, and named *Meconopsis betonicifolia* by the French botanist Franchet. George Forrest had also come across it, but at no time had any seed been collected.

Although he was on the look-out for Bailey's poppy, Kingdon-Ward did not connect the two, except to remark to himself that he doubted if the Colonel's plant was any better than his discovery. He was in any case diverted by the rhododendrons frothing with purple, scarlet, white and pink flowers, and the wealth of primulas. Here they found *Primula florindae* growing four feet tall, its swaying stems crowded with great heads of pale yellow flowers; and *Primula sikkimensis,* in its full colour spectrum from cream to purple, bejewelled the meadows. Bright blue and white meconopsis flowers mingled together, and scarlet rhododendrons lit the hills. They reached Tumbatse, to find it set in a valley which was a plant-collector's paradise. It was here, he knew, that Bailey had found his poppy, and in a tangled thicket of roses, willows and other shrubs, he discovered clumps of that same *Meconopsis*. He recalled:

> The plants even out of flower were conspicuous enough with their large basal leaves covered with a bronze-chest-nut fur; in bloom, with one or two sky-blue flowers swinging from the tall leafy stem – and at their best there might be six or eight flowers together on one stem – even the least observant could hardly fail to notice and to remark upon so unusual a plant.

156

He also realized that these and the poppy he had spotted by the track two days earlier were the same species.

After a period of blissful botanizing, the expedition pressed on to the Tsangpo gorge, entering a terrain never before visited by Europeans. It was a wild, surrealistic landscape of towering cliffs, huge boulders scattered as casually as shingle on a beach, and thick forest. The climbs they had to make up sheer precipices filled Kingdon-Ward with horror, but despite this he managed to collect seed as he went, including that of *Rhododendron maddeni*. They found the Falls of the Brahmaputra which proved to be relatively small, dwarfs compared with the size of the Victoria Falls in Africa and the Niagara Falls in America, but the journey in itself was a triumph and established Kingdon-Ward as a major explorer as well as plant hunter.

In the autumn he harvested a large quantity of *Meconopis* seeds and took them home to England. When the first plants to flower in Britain were exhibited at a meeting of the Royal Horticultural Society they created a sensation, setting Kingdon-Ward high up in the league table of plant collectors. But while the horticultural world was keen to lionize him, he was eager to return to the rugged Asian mountains, with all their beauty and dangers.

In 1926 his reputation as a collector earned him the support of a group of wealthy gardening enthusiasts, among them Lionel de Rothschild, who was devoted to rhododendrons. He also received grants for an expedition from The Royal Society, the same august scientific body that had backed Sir Joseph Banks as the naturalist for the historic round-the-world voyage of the *Endeavour* in 1768. The trip took Kingdon-Ward to remote parts of Burma and Assam, areas which were to become his special preserve. Vividly he described the North-East Frontier between India and Burma as 'the edge of the world'.

It was during this journey that he found the tea-rose primula (*Primula agleniana var. thearose*) growing in the mountains of the Irrawaddy-Brahmaputra Divide. He had been climbing all day through dense, ancient forest, which was dank and cold. Suddenly the trees ended as abruptly as the margin of an

157

English copse, and he and his party strode out on to an alpine clearing where the light was heightened by great banks of snow gradually melting into the vivid new spring growth of the meadow. The pitching of tents and the brewing of tea seemed to take an unconscionable time to Kingdon-Ward, who was impatient to start searching for plants. With only half an hour of daylight left, he crossed a snow-bridge to a steep bank which led to the cliffs surrounding the camp. There, right on the snow line, he saw a 'vivid blush pink flower . . . as big as a rose, and of the fresh clear pink seen in Madame Butterfly' [the name of a hybrid tea-rose]. It was the tea-rose primula, a truly magnificent sight, as he wrote in his book, *Plant Hunting on the Edge of the World*:

> I can recall several flowers which at first sight have knocked the breath out of me, but only two or three which have taken me by storm as did this one. The sudden vision is like a physical blow, a blow in the pit of the stomach; one can only gasp and stare. In the face of such un-surpassed loveliness one is afraid to move, as with bated breath one mutters the single word 'God!' – a prayer rather than an exclamation. And when at last with fluttering heart one does venture to step forward, it is on tiptoe, and hat in hand, to wonder and to worship.

The primula grew among many other fine members of the same genus – *Primula involucrata wardii, P. microdonta alpicola, P. florindae, P. silaensis, P. melandonta, P. beesiana*, as well as *Rhododendron sanguineum, R. fragariflorum, R. lysolepsis* and *R. riparium* – while pinguiculas and cassiopes studded the turf.

In 1928 he made a second journey to this remote region. On this occasion he was deserted by most of his porters, who took away with them a large quantity of rations, leaving Kingdon-Ward and the remainder of his coolies desperately short of food. Only six out of twenty-seven of them had remained faithful, and because of the intense cold on the route to Assam he had to share his clothes with them. Nevertheless, it was during this expedition that he found *Nomocharis aperta*, with its large, lily-like, starfish-shaped flowers heavily spotted with a rich purple on a pinkish-white ground. Botanically it was an important find, since it was the first of the genus to be discovered in Assam. Together the two expeditions to Assam and Burma produced a vast haul of fine plants, with eighty-five different species coming from just three valleys.

Like Richard Spruce in the Amazon, Kingdon-Ward had to contend with a variety of voracious seed-eaters. In 1930 he was travelling with Lord Cranbrook, an enthusiastic amateur zoologist, tracing the course of the River Taron, one of the headwaters of the Irrawaddy. Their route took them through country particularly rich in gentians, deep blue trumpet-shaped flowers, including *Gentiana wardii*, *G. veitchiorum* and *G. gilvostriata*. He had twice discovered the latter, but on each occasion had failed to bring home any ripe seed. This time he was determined to succeed, and despite having a large collection of the seeds attacked by scores of ravenous voles and mice (which, when he devised a defensive screen of traps, simply moved to the tent where he was drying another batch), he got some of them home at last.

Throughout his long career his fear of heights never deserted him. During a trip across Southern Tibet in 1935 he had to traverse a rock face which sloped down to a knife-edged ledge, below which was a drop of thousands of feet to the river below. Four toe-holds chipped out of the granite were the only aid. Kingdon-Ward recorded that when he looked at what he had to cross, 'it made me giddy, and I shrank back with that awful stab in the pit of the stomach which sudden fear can induce – as though one had been violently kicked in the solar plexus'. The only way to get across was to rely on balance, and he knew he could not achieve that. In the end he did make the crossing with the help of a rope and the encouragement of his porters, who swung themselves across the glassy rock-face with the agility of spiders.

Two years later, in Burma, he was trying to scale a mountain, Ka Karpo, when he had to jump a wide crack in the rock. If he had fallen short he would have plunged some three thousand feet into the valley below. Before he made the jump, he recalled, 'my courage was oozing faster than the sawdust from a torn doll'. During the same expedition he slipped off the edge of a mountain track, only to be saved by being impaled through his armpit on a bamboo. Because bamboos can be very poisonous he had to pour iodine into the wound to sterilize it.

Kingdon-Ward was fifty-four when the Second World War broke out. He was in London during one of his rare visits home, and immediately volunteered, suggesting that he would be most useful working for the Government of India. With what seemed to be an uncanny talent for making the wrong decisions, the authorities again set him to work as a censor, possibly the most boring job offered by war. He therefore joined the Home Guard, and taking part in their exercises helped him to feel he was making a positive contribution to the war effort.

With the entry of the Japanese into the war, Kingdon-Ward was attached to the Special Operations Executive with the rank of temporary captain, and at the end of 1941 was sent to Singapore to advise on ways of holding up the enemy as it advanced on the colony. Shortly before the fall of Singapore he was hurriedly sent on a secret mission to discover a way from India, through Burma, to China, which could be used to move men and equipment during the rainy season to open up a new front against the now-dominant Japanese Imperial Army. Throughout 1942 and 1943 he disappeared completely. His family received no letters or any kind of communication from him, and all that the War Office would say was that it believed he was somewhere in Burma. In fact he was tramping over hundreds of miles of rugged country, seeking out routes for the allied troops. During the latter part of the war he worked as an instructor at the School of Jungle Warfare in Poona in India, mainly teaching survival skills to airmen. After the war he was employed by the American Government to track down their crashed military aircraft in the jungles between Assam and Burma.

Despite swearing that he would never marry again, in 1947 he did. His new wife was Jean Macklin, and their honeymoon was spent travelling to Manipur, where Kingdon-Ward embarked on his seventeenth expedition. His wife, who was a good deal younger than he, was his constant companion during his last collecting trips.

As so often with his plant-hunting forays, he set himself the target of a particular plant. In this case it was a mysterious specimen that, by its appearance, could be either a lily or a nomocharis. When he had been searching for crashed American aircraft after the war, he had climbed the Sirhoi Kashong, an eight-thousand-foot mountain towering out of the Manipur hills, from which it was possible to see the Chindwin river. On the mountainside he had found the lily/nomocharis in seed, and collected the few capsules left, and also dug up some bulbs which flowered later in the Residency garden in Imphal. They proved to be wretched, weak-looking things, but did present an interesting botanical riddle which stirred up a considerable argument among scientists. Kingdon-Ward was fairly convinced it was a lily new to cultivation, and he referred to it as the Sirhoi lily or the Manipur lily.

After a number of the inevitable interruptions, he and his wife reached the Sirhoi Kashong and rediscovered the lily. They saw it in flower, and later dug up a fairly large number of bulbs and collected a quantity of seed. These were sent home to England, and the seed, which was sown under glass at the Royal Horticultural Society Gardens at Wisley in Surrey, produced flowering plants in fifteen months. Horticulturally the reports were not encouraging, though: the blooms were described unflatteringly as 'dirty white'. They appeared very different from those that Kingdon-Ward had described flowering in their hundreds in the wild. He wrote that 'The buds are almost carmine, but when they open the inside takes on a pale blush-pink, the outside (which has a radiant satiny sheen) being rose-purple.' Now that they had living material to work on, the botanists eventually agreed that it was a lily; and it was named *Lilium mackliniae,* in honour of his wife. In 1950 it was exhibited at the Chelsea Flower Show in London. It was a delicate pink in cultivation, and greatly improved upon its first flowerings. It attracted considerable public attention and admiration, and was awarded a Royal Horticultural Society Award of Merit.

Three months after his lily's public triumph, Kingdon-Ward was again roaming the wilderness, and facing the greatest danger of his long career. For about four weeks the whole of Eastern India, West Bengal, Assam and Bihar had been repeatedly shaken by minor earthquakes, but on 15 August came a massive one, described in *The Times* as 'one of the most gigantic seismological events of the century'. In Assam alone a thousand people died, and five million were made homeless. Pilots flying over the area reported that a chain of mountains on the Indo-Burmese-Chinese border had disappeared. The Subansiri river in Assam vanished into huge crevices, and four days later erupted out of the ground, flooding thousands of acres, destroying crops and houses, and driving the people into the trees for safety. Roads were torn apart, and railway tracks were bent and buckled as though made of plasticine. (In Istanbul a seismograph actually broke, and at a seismological station in Dorking in England the oscillations on the recording instruments were so violent that the records were too blurred to read.)

When the full fury of the earthquake struck, the Kingdon-Wards and their small party were camped outside Rima (now Ch'a-yu in China, but at that time still part of Assam), about half a mile from the Lohit river and less than fifty miles from the epicentre of the earthquake. For safety and convenience they had pitched the three tents they were using close to one another on a patch of sand. All around were high mountains, so that they were in a sheltered bowl. The earth tremors of the past few weeks did not seem serious, indeed they were almost the norm for the area, and they calmly prepared for the night, all set to move on the following morning to make a plant-collecting assault on the alpine slopes.

Recalling the event in the Indian newspaper, *The Statesman*, Kingdon-Ward wrote:

> At about eight o'clock local time, on the evening of August 15, I was writing my diary and thinking joyfully of tomorrow's march up the Lati Gorge, towards the

Burma frontier, which lay due east. I reckoned we should
camp the first night in the gorge at about seven thousand
feet, the second night at nine thousand or ten thousand
feet amidst a wealth of temperate flowers. My wife was
reading in bed.

The night was clear, starlit and utterly peaceful and silent but for
a sharp, bright wind that gusted down from the mountain-tops.
Then, suddenly, it began: noises of rending, grinding, roaring
and thundering were heard, so huge and loud that for a moment
they could not understand what was happening. It was Jean
Kingdon-Ward who first yelled 'earthquake!'; they grabbed the
hurricane lamp and ran outside; immediately they were thrown
to the heaving, writhing ground. All around them the mountains
were blurred and trembling, being jostled to and fro like giant
jellies, and from deep within the earth there was a terrifying
hammering. Their two Sherpa porters had also rushed from
their tents and been hurled to the ground, and the four of them
lay on the bounding earth, holding hands for comfort, while
rocks poured down the mountainsides. Kingdon-Ward described the experience:

> We knew that we were helpless, and the surprising thing
> is that we talked so calmly to each other, frightened out of
> our wits as we were. I had the feeling that we were lying
> on a thin cake of rock crust which separated us from the
> boiling interior of the earth and that this crust was about
> to break up like an ice-flow in spring, hurling us to a
> horrible death.

The earthquake lasted for about five minutes, although it
seemed an eternity, and for a long time afterwards rocks and
boulders continued to cascade down from the shattered mountains. A pall of dust blotted out the night sky, and for days
afterwards virtually extinguished the sun, while distant explo-
sions echoed through the valleys.

The next day they could see the extent of the damage. Rima
was in ruins, and the River Lohit and a small tributary were
floods of liquid mud. Paddy fields had been drained and much of

the terraced agricultural land had slipped away. All the bridges over the Lohit had been destroyed, so the party was trapped until a battered patrol of eight men from the Assam Rifles fought their way through to them, and rigged up a rope-bridge.

Exactly a month after the earthquake, the Kingdon-Wards and their party reached Walong, the last outpost of India. Despite the horrors of the journey and the dreadful devastation all around them, they did manage to collect one fine plant, the yellow-flowered *Cornus chinensis*. From Walong they made their way to Sadiya and Shillong, an arduous trek, and eventually arrived in England early in 1951.

Political unrest throughout the Far East was gradually closing down Kingdon-Ward's hunting grounds; the age of the seeker of fine garden plants was drawing to a close. He was so depressed by the outlook for the future that he even applied for a job in the Civil Service in London, but was turned down because, at sixty-six, he was too old. For a while he toyed with the idea of shifting his territory to Papua, which was relatively untouched, but his tentative plans came to nothing. Burma and Assam still beckoned, and in the end North Burma was selected for another trip, despite official objections.

Kingdon-Ward and his wife reached the territory two days before Christmas Day 1952. It was a journey punctuated with the usual problems and minor incidents, such as getting lost in a rhododendron forest, but on his sixty-eighth birthday he distinguished himself by climbing over 11,000 feet up Burma's Tagulum Bum. The trip produced a fine haul of plants, including more than thirty species of rhododendron and almost a hundred other species, including a superb honeysuckle with gigantic flowers, *Lonicera hildebrandiana*. Quite outstanding among them was an epiphytic lily, *Lilium arboricola,* which makes its home in trees. The last wild lily to be discovered, it is a delicate plant that will grow only under glass. Its Turk's-cap blooms look as though they are cut out of translucent green silk.

Sixty-eight might have seemed a reasonable age to retire from a way of life that would be exhausting for a man half as old, but two months after his seventieth birthday Kingdon-Ward set off once again, this time for the Southern Chin Hills in Burma on a commission from the Gothenburg Botanic Gardens in Sweden, accompanied by a Swedish botanist. The expedition produced a good harvest of seeds, some fine orchids and a useful herbarium collection but, compared with those of his past journeys, these were minor achievements. However, Kingdon-Ward's patrons were pleased with what he brought back to Sweden, and he was invited to lecture at Uppsala where the great Linnaeus had worked and held court for so long.

During 1957 he spent most of his time in London vaguely contemplating another journey, but his plans were now little more than those of an old man reluctant to lessen his grip on the past. The hardship of his travels and recurrent bouts of fever had taken their toll, and early in 1958 he was suddenly taken ill and rushed to hospital. On April 6 he lapsed into a coma, and died two days later, with a long full career behind him. He will always be remembered by those who appreciate his great contribution to the gardens of the world.

JOSEPH ROCK (1884-1962)

Few diseases produce such a predictable reaction – that of fear and disgust – as leprosy. The very idea of being infected with something which slowly eats away the body is loathsome, and tradition and history have stigmatized the sufferers as unclean and unfit to remain in society. It is little wonder, then, that generations have sought a cure.

It was in a way appropriate that Joseph Rock was chosen, as Agricultural Explorer in charge of the Office of Foreign Seed and Plant Introduction at the United States Department of Agriculture, to hunt down the true chaulmoogra tree, the source of the drug which would bring relief to the people whom leprosy set aside from the rest of mankind. Rock, who was born in Vienna in 1884, knew all too well the anguish and suffering caused by rejection. His mother, Franciska, a warm, affectionate woman of Austro-Hungarian descent, died when he was six, and her mother died two weeks later, leaving Joseph to be raised by his sister, Karolina, and his father, Franz Seraph, who was a gloomy, dominating religious maniac who made his wife's death the excuse for eccentric and morbid behaviour. Joseph was haunted by the memory of being made to put a flower between his mother's cold, stiff fingers as she lay in an open coffin, and throughout his childhood his father forced him to kneel and weep at his mother's graveside.

A poorly educated man and a baker by trade, Franz Rock became steward to a Polish nobleman, Count Potocki, who had a winter home in Vienna. Devoting all his spare time to religious exercises, Franz installed an altar in his quarters and made his two children act out the Mass daily. He never demonstrated the slightest warmth or affection towards his son and daughter, although he did make a considerable fuss of an older, illegitimate son.

Against such a background it was scarcely surprising that Joseph grew into a strange, introverted child. Although intelligent, he took little interest in his lessons and was a persistent truant. He allowed his imagination to construct a private world which protected him from the increasingly weird behaviour of his father. It was a world in which China became his fantasy land, and when he was only thirteen he began to teach himself Chinese, in which he became fluent. China eventually became his home, although his love-hate relationship with it was of the most passionate nature. As his school days drew to a close he wanted nothing more than to be allowed to join the navy, but his father had decided he was to be a priest. It was the seminary or nothing, so Joseph left home and spent the next three years living off his wits in Europe and North Africa.

In 1904 his father died. There was now little to hold him in Vienna, since he was not particularly close to his sister or half-brother, so for the next year he travelled in Italy, Tunisia and Malta and then, on an impulse, worked his passage to New York as a ships' steward. In New York he worked as a dishwasher, went down with consumption, and after treatment took a series of jobs in hotels in the Adirondack mountains, before moving on to Texas. Although he found menial work extremely distasteful, he spent the time usefully, perfecting his English. Towards the end of 1907 he sailed for Hawaii in a vessel with a suitably oriental name, the *Manchuria*, losing on board what little money he had in a dice game organized by a Chinaman, who did even worse and cut his own throat to save face.

Hawaii was a turning point in his life. He managed to get a job teaching Latin and natural history at Mills School, which became the Mid-Pacific Institute. Being largely ignorant of natural history, he had to work twice as hard as his students, tutoring himself so that he could keep a step ahead of them. But his do-it-yourself course led to a job with the Hawaii forestry service, collecting herbarium material and seeds of rare local shrubs and trees. It was a perfect preparation for his future career.

In 1913 Rock became an American citizen and in 1919 he was appointed Professor of Systematic Botany at the University of Hawaii. It was a title he treasured. Although he claimed to have been to the University of Vienna, in fact he had never been an undergraduate. His fluent command of Hungarian, Italian, French, Latin, Greek, Chinese and Arabic, as well as English and his native German, was self-taught. He could even write Sanskrit. But despite these achievements, he felt inferior to his fellow academics, and needed to invent his university career to keep even with them, even though, over a ten-year period, he published over forty works on botany, and established himself among the leaders in his field. Eventually he was offered the post with the US Department of Agriculture, which was to send him to look for the chaulmoogra, or kalaw, tree.

The actual whereabouts of the fruit-bearing trees was something of a mystery, which was further compounded by the different names given them. On investigation it also became clear that the seeds of more than one species were used, while the only true chaulmoogra oil came from the seed of *Taraktogenos kurzii*. In India and other parts of the East, lepers had for hundreds of years been treated with the oil which was expressed from the seeds of a fruit that grew deep in the forests and jungles. Having been collected by tribespeople and sold to merchants, the seeds eventually found their way to the bazaars, and were usually in pretty poor condition by the time they reached the customer.

An Indian legend describes their discovery. Long before Buddha came to Earth, a king in Northern India, Ok-sa-ga-rit, enraged the sons and daughters of his first queen by naming a son by his second queen as his heir. Angrily, his other children left the kingdom. They had not long been in exile before the eldest sister, Piya, contracted leprosy. Her brothers took her deep into the forest to a cave where she could live without being rejected and abused as the disease destroyed her beauty.

Meanwhile, in Benares, Rama, the king there, also became a leper and, abdicating in favour of his son, sought solitude in the same forest as Piya. He lived in a hollow tree and ate the plants that grew about him, in particular the leaves and fruit of the kalaw tree. Gradually his leprosy disappeared and he realized the cure had been brought about by the apparently magical properties of the tree.

One day as he was walking in the forest he heard a terrified scream. It came from Piya's cave where she was being attacked by a tiger. Fortunately the entrance was too narrow to allow the animal to seize her. Rama went to her rescue and, seeing her condition, fed her on the roots, leaves and fruit of the kalaw until she, too, was cured. They married and she bore him thirty-two sons.

Until 1918 Western medicine largely ignored chaulmoogra oil. That year Dr A. L. Dean, a distinguished professor of chemistry and President of the University of Hawaii, subjected the oil to laboratory analysis and prepared it for the treatment of lepers. The first patients were given intramuscular injections and oral doses. The latter method was soon discontinued because it produced violent sickness, but the injections scored a high success rate. What was quite evident was that there would never be sufficient oil if the traditional source of supply had to be depended upon. It was essential that the wild stands of *Taraktogenos kurzii* and its relatives should be found and studied, and seeds collected for propagation so that plantations could be established; and in 1920 Rock was chosen for the task.

His search for the chaulmoogra tree involved careful detective work. Investigations showed that seeds were coming on to the market from Burma and Lower Bengal, as well as from Assam. It was also evident that seeds came from three different species of trees with very similar oil to that of *Taraktogenos kurzii*. There was much confusion, and only the tree producing the true chaulmoogra oil had to be found and cultivated if the substance was to become a major weapon in the fight against leprosy.

In a bulletin of the US Department of Agriculture, Rock wrote of his objective:

> . . . to locate *Taraktogenos kurzii* in its native habitat and look up especially all those localities from which Tarakto-genos seeds were brought to European chemists in India, in order to ascertain whether or not the seeds they are using are those of this species. *Taraktogenos kurzii* is evidently widely distributed in Burma. Numerous locali-ties were given where kalaw trees may be found, as, for example, in Burma, at Chongnakwa, Lower Burma, and also at Tabyo.

Rock began his journey by sailing from America to Singapore, where he took the train to Bangkok, over a thousand miles away. The train took five days, and he spent his nights at rest-houses which were spaced out along the track. He stayed in Bangkok for some time, visiting temples and attending a Royal garden party, before making his way north to the sacred Doi Sootep mountain. Its forests were a welcome protection from the merciless sun; and he wrote about the ascent in the March 1922 edition of the American *National Geographic Magazine*:

> . . . [it] is at first steep and rocky. Gorgeous flowering crape myrtle trees border the trail, while higher up Diperocarpaceae, with mighty trunks and spreading crowns, give the landscape a bold aspect. Nature writes its story with a mighty hand, and orchids and graceful vines on the wayside are the commas and exclamation points of a harmonious composition. It would require a book of many pages to tell the story of the flora of this wonderful mountain.

At the summit was a superb temple, the approach to which he described thus:

> No stone stairway lined with marble pillars or wayside shrines, but living columns of pines festooned and gar-landed with sweet-scented orchids and vines, the steps

covered with a living carpet of velvet moss; no organ played by human hands, but gentle breezes whispering in the trees and a chorus provided by feathered songsters whose abode is in the mighty fronded canopy surrounding the hallowed spot.

Rock was given to high-flown phrases and was often the despair of his editors, but nevertheless it was an idyllic spot. He camped in the forest under pines, oaks and giant chestnuts, from all of which he collected seeds.

While still a child, Joseph Rock had begun to assume a rather grand manner, largely influenced by the luxurious life that he observed his father's master Count Potocki enjoying, and throughout his career as a botanical and ethnographic explorer, he insisted on travelling in some style. Wherever he was in the wilderness he would complete his day by relaxing in his Abercrombie and Fitch folding bath. Whenever he received even the most humble village headman, he was always impeccably dressed in a spotless white shirt, tie and jacket. His fastidiousness extended to his eating habits, too: every night in camp his table would be spread with laundered linen, and he dined on Austrian dishes that he had trained his servants to cook.

From the mountains he travelled to the town of Korat which he used as a base while he collected fruit and herbarium material from the maikrabao tree (*Hydnocarpus anthelmintica*), whose seeds were sold as those of the chaulmoogra, before going northwest to Chiangmai, 300 miles away. Here he chartered a houseboat to sail down the Meh Ping river south to Rahaeng. At first the journey was glorious: the boat slipped past banks thick with bamboos and silk-cotton trees, before the river squeezed itself into deep gorges between beautiful forest-clad mountain slopes, 'which were here and there crowned by a wat or small Buddhist shrine glistening in the sunlight'. Rock described this leisurely journey:

Many times during the day I would stop the boat and climb the mountains to explore the forests and collect plants. Legends are connected with many places along this river and one spot on a semi-barren mountain slope is pointed out to the traveller as the place where Buddha crossed this hill with a fighting cock, which scratched the surface of the ground to such an extent as to leave these places bare today.

The boat often ran aground on sandbanks, which Rock found intensely frustrating. On one occasion he stripped to his underpants and plunged overboard, planning to swim gently along until the boat caught up with him, but desperate cries from the skipper persuaded him to return, and he was told that the water was swarming with crocodiles. Then, for two days they had to battle with rapids, while they raced through forests of gigantic bamboos. One night a herd of elephants came to the river bank to feed on these plants, and the sound like gunfire of the shoots being snapped off prevented the travellers from sleeping. On another day, botanizing on shore, Rock was driven off the mountainside by an angry bear.

Eventually they reached Rahaeng, where Rock reluctantly parted with his boat and crew. Ahead lay a long journey to Moulmein through Mesawt, the last settlement before the border into Burma, over mountains densely clothed with teak, oaks and bamboo. After crossing the border, the next leg of the journey took him over the Kawkereik Hills, which were extremely rich botanically. Here he found his first true chaulmoogra oil tree, but not in fruit. He arrived at Moulmein at the mouth of the Salween river in the Gulf of Martaban on Christmas Eve, 1920, regretting at first that he was not going to spend Christmas in the forests, but delighted later to join the American missionaries in the city for the festival.

From Moulmein he made his way to the village of Oktada in the Martaban Hills, where he was assured the kalaw tree grew in its thousands. He wrote of the day he arrived here, trekking up the bed of a dry stream which was littered with huge quartz rocks:

> In the crevices between these enormous boulders, often ten feet high or more, there grew in great abundance a

tree which was loaded with young fruits, then the size of a tennis ball and covered with a fawn-coloured tomentum. The natives stated that when the fruits matured they became much darker. The trees observed had a height of about eighty or ninety feet and their size was much greater in every respect than that accredited to *Taraktogenos kurzii*.

The tree was, in fact, *Hydnocarpus catanea,* another of the chaulmoogra look-alikes, but he collected seed from the few mature fruits he found so that the oil could be tested.

From Oktada, Rock headed for Rangoon, more determined than ever to find the healing tree. The Rangoon Forest Office told him the species was to be found 400 miles away in the Upper Chindwin district, particularly in the area around Mawlaik near the Indian border, so, with a Madrassi cook and a Mohammedan boy to look after him, he took the train north to Amarapura, crossed the Irrawaddy river to Sagaing (near Mandalay) and from there continued by train across semi-desert to Monywa on the Upper Chindwin river.

Monywa offended his fastidious nature. The dust was so thick that the bullock cart taking his luggage to the steamer, a stern-wheeler that would take him on by river, disappeared completely in the dust-storm stirred up by the plodding animals. He visited the market, which he found appalling:

> The bazaar is a living entomological collection. Never, not even in Egypt, have I seen flies so numerous. They cover the conical piles of brown sugar spread out on mats on the ground to such an extent that almost every grain is moving, and this in the midst of squatting, betel-nut chewing, and expectorating women, surrounded by the mangiest fighting dogs, rotten tomatoes, cauliflower, cabbages and cucurbits.

He was therefore delighted to get aboard the steamer and out on to the river. He enjoyed the experience even though they ran aground on a sandbank, an occupational hazard of river travel in the East, and the third-class passengers were dumped on the

muddy shore to lighten the vessel. From his first-class ac-
commodation he could enjoy the 'deep purples, green, light
blue, yellow, dark gray [sic], and light pinks, with an occasional
sombre yellowish-brown denoting a shaven priest' of the
'wonderfully picturesque . . . gaily coloured costumes of the
Burmese men and women' as they waded and scrambled up the
grey mud-banks of the river. And there were other fascinating
sights, such as the raft with a house in the middle and a flagstaff
made from a growing tree, and the houseboat as big as an
ocean-going junk.

Eventually Rock reached Mawlaik on the Chindwin, and
hurried to the Forestry Office, where he was informed that 'the
presence of *Taraktogenos kurzii* is known to us only through
natives who take out licences for collecting the seeds, after the
rainy season, in three localities'. One of these was fifty miles
away at Mainyaung, another at Khoung Kyew, and the third at
Kyokta. He decided to head for Khoung Kyew, and having
hired a dugout canoe he set off down the Chindwin. The
journey was in dense fog, and soon he had to leave the river.
With twenty coolies, most of them women carrying babies on
their backs and his equipment on their heads, he travelled for two
days overland to Khoung Kyew, where he was told the tree
grew in the denser parts of the forest. Guided by the headman,
and accompanied by an interpreter and a number of coolies,
he continued on foot along the bed of a shallow stream into the
forest. At last he found *Taraktogenos kurzii,* growing in loamy
quartz sand. The trees, many of them sixty feet tall, were
spread over an area of some forty acres. The forest floor was thick
with a profusion of ferns, and a variety of *Thunbergia* (black-
eyed Susan) clambered through the trees. Wild elephants
roamed the forest and doused themselves in the stream Rock and
his party had used as a highway. Unfortunately, not a single
taraktogenos fruit was to be found.

Wearily Rock broke camp and trudged on to the village of
Kyokta, which comprised a square of thirty flimsy thatched
houses and a pagoda constructed from woven bamboo. Here he
was graciously received by the headman and elders of the

village, who did everything they could to make his visit pleasant. After spending a night there, and determined not to return to his base without a load of chaulmoogra seeds, he plunged into the forest with thirty-six coolies. There had been so many disappointments that he felt sure this time he would know success. For six miles they walked along the bed of a dried-up stream, hemmed in on both sides by a solid wall of green. As the banks grew steeper, he realized that they were completely clothed with *Taraktogenos kurzii*. Once again he searched the branches in vain for fruit, but a closer look on the ground beneath the trees revealed quantities of seed. He was lucky to find any seeds at all: the native collectors had been through the area, and those that they missed were usually eaten by monkeys, bears, or rooting pigs, and those that fell into the streams and rivers were eaten by fish.

Tigers and elephants made collecting dangerous, particularly as the harvest tended to coincide with the mating season, which made them particularly aggressive. Rock split his coolies into small parties and set them to scour the ground, which produced a fine haul of seeds. He was happy and light-hearted, but his cheerful mood turned to one of unease when the party discovered that it had been shadowed into the forest by a tiger. He recalled:

> When we reached the stream bed up which we had come a few hours previously, we found that a large tiger had followed us into the jungle, for there were its footprints so clear and distinct that I stopped and photographed them. We had no arms with us; only a camera and quantities of Chaulmoogra seeds.

In spite of this, they returned to the village without mishap, and Rock busied himself with packing his precious seeds in powdered charcoal and oiled paper. This was to prevent them dehydrating on their long journeys to Honolulu, Washington D.C., the Philippines and Singapore, where they were to be germinated. Time was vital, since it was known that the seeds very quickly became sterile if allowed to dry out. His plan was to leave the following morning and rush the seeds to Mawlaik for shipment to America, from where they would be distributed.

At dawn the next day he was preparing to leave, when the headman came with terrible news: a five-year-old boy had told them that his mother had been killed in the night by a tiger. He was the son of one of Rock's coolies, whose wives and children had stayed to harvest the grain from the rice paddies while they had gone in search of the chaulmoogra seeds. The families had spent the night in a rough shelter by the field, where they had been attacked by the tiger, almost certainly the same animal that had stalked Rock and his men up the dry river bed. The child had returned to the village with five claw wounds on his back and his left leg badly burned as a result of being hurled into a fire by the tiger.

The whole village was roused by the beating of gongs and temple drums. Clearly Rock knew he could not leave at such a time of crisis and suffering: 'All the male villagers armed themselves with spears and knives and marching ahead of them, I went to the scene of the tragedy', he wrote. The sight that greeted him was horrible. With only one entrance, the hut had offered no escape when the tiger charged in, and three women, the little boy and a baby girl of two had been trapped. One woman, her face bitten away, was found dead about a hundred yards from the shelter, another with hideous face wounds lay just alive outside – she died soon afterwards – while a third was a mangled corpse inside. The little girl had been carried off by the tiger. Rock did what he could for the woman who was still alive, while the men built a stout wooden trap and baited it with one of the bodies.

The village priest insisted that Rock should sleep in the temple for safety, but no one was to have any peace that night. A tremendous storm broke out, and the noise of rain and thunder was combined with the sound of elephants trumpeting, and the wild cries and yells of men. In the morning Rock stepped out of the little woven temple to a scene of devastation. A herd of elephants had come to the village, destroyed houses and rice stores, and eaten much of the hard-won harvest. The only good thing that had happened that terrible night was the capture of the

tiger. So great was its lust for human flesh that it had broken
through the bamboo screen separating the trap from the body of
the dead woman, and had eaten nearly all of it. Screaming and
spitting, it was speared to death by the villagers and carried back
in triumph to the shattered settlement.

After Rock's pioneering search and his discovery of *Taraktogenos kurzii*, the tree was also discovered growing wild in Assam
and Eastern Bengal; but his success had established him firmly as
a plant collector. During the years that followed he travelled
widely in the East, particularly China, and collected a vast
amount of herbarium and horticultural material. Although he
harvested great quantities of rhododendron seed, he failed to
discover much that was new, but he will certainly be remembered
for the glowing pink flowers of *Paeonia suffruticosa* 'Rock's
variety', which he discovered and introduced.

Despite the fact that, during the long period Rock made
China his home there was hardly a moment of peace, his love
of China intensified over the years. In his early days there he was
constantly in danger from the bandit gangs that ranged the
mountains in the Likiang district, where he did most of his
collecting. If it was not bandits, it was war-lords: the civil
war between the Nationalists and the Communists, at its height
during the 1930s, had started when Mao-tse-Tung began
organizing the peasants of Hunan province in 1921, and resulted
in Rock's exile in 1949 from China and the home he had made in
Likiang, where, he said, he wanted to die 'among those beautiful
mountains rather than in a bleak hospital bed all alone'.

In 1922 he explored in the Mekong valley, and made his
way to Muli where he discovered *Rhododendron chryseum*,
then known as *muliense*, a dwarf form with aromatic leaves and
trusses of bright yellow flowers. Mostly, though, he was hampered in his work by various disturbances. In 1925 he was caught
up in a bloody war between Moslems and Tibetans. The
Tibetans attacked a Moslem garrison at Labrang and dis-
embowelled the captured soldiers, and when the Moslems
recaptured the town they proceeded to massacre the Tibetans
with machine-guns.

On a journey to Chengtu in Szechuan in 1927, along an ancient caravan route, his party was attacked by bandits. Fortunately they were driven off by the forty soldiers accompanying him, but the next day they were attacked again in a mountain pass, and had to retreat into the woods. The day after that, he and his soldiers found themselves fighting a running gun battle with the brigands. As he approached the city of Chaotung in Kweichow Province, the party was met by 250 soldiers who had been sent by the local magistrate to rescue them, so Rock, with an escort of over 300 soldiers, was able to make a rather triumphant entry into the city. This of course suited his penchant for travelling in some style. His parties always tended to be much larger than those of his fellow collectors; and when he left Chengtu his caravan was half a mile long.

Although China always remained the land of his dreams, he was shocked and offended by the cruelty he witnessed wherever he went. In the little kingdom of Muli he discovered dungeons in the palace where prisoners were kept in appalling conditions, their heads locked into huge wooden collars which made it impossible for them to lie down. He complained bitterly to the King, and managed to have one prisoner released.

During 1928 and 1929 he spent much of his time collecting in mountains around Minya Konka, collecting thousands of plants, nearly 800 bird-skins, and taking hundreds of colour and black-and-white photographs.

Gradually ethnography superseded botany as his major interest. He made a minutely detailed study of the Nakhi tribe of China, learning their language and producing a dictionary, and published his research and findings in a classic work of scholarship, *The Ancient Na-khi Kingdom of Southwest China.*

Joseph Rock was in many ways a sad figure. No doubt as a result of his upbringing, he found it impossible to give or receive affection, and love certainly passed him by. He felt constantly persecuted, particularly when he was abused for being a foreigner by the Chinese. He fancied that his genius went unrecognized by fellow academics, and was often driven to the point of suicide; at least in his letters and diaries he frequently threatens to take his own life. In fact he never even made the attempt, but died from a heart attack at the age of seventy-eight on 5 December 1962, in Hawaii, the island from which he had first set out on the road to becoming a botanist-explorer.

EPILOGUE

The 1914-18 war saw the beginning of the end of the great days of plant hunting. Fewer major gardens were being created than in the preceding period and, as many existing ones were abandoned or sold for development, support for expeditions from private subscribers and nursery gardens began to decrease.

After the war, although plant hunters such as Forrest, Farrer and Kingdon-Ward were still searching for good garden plants and rarities for specialist collectors (while dodging revolutions and the political upheavals which were reaching out even to the most remote parts of the world), gradually the emphasis was shifting. Plants for a purely economic purpose were becoming more desirable, and the backing for expeditions was beginning to come from government departments and scientific institutions rather than private sponsors. Botanists were now briefed to seek out species which might be drug sources for medical research or material for plant breeders engaged in developing disease-resistant and heavy-cropping hybrids for food production: potatoes were to be more highly prized than primulas.

This has not meant, however, that the search for beautiful plants does not continue: after the Second World War, the late Paul Furze introduced many splendid bulbous plants, including some superb irises and alliums, from Iran, Turkey and Afghanistan; Brian Mathew of Kew Gardens has collected widely in

Europe and the Near East, specializing in irises and crocuses; and Roy Lancaster has followed in the Himalayan footsteps of Wilson and Forrest, collecting the plants of that region.

Collectors today are even more hampered by politics than their forebears were. Throughout the world, countries have closed their borders, or placed restrictions on travel within their boundaries. Only if isolationism is abandoned will plant hunters again be able to explore some of the richest plant areas still remaining in the world, and reintroduce many fine species that have disappeared from cultivation.

Modern expeditions are much speedier affairs than in the past. There are no long sea journeys, and little slogging by foot or mule over endless rugged miles of often barren wilderness to reach some remote area abundant in plants. No longer does the plant hunter have to spend a year or more in a territory, first to collect the flowering specimens, and then to return for the seeds. Botanists now fly from one international airport to another, and then travel by light aircraft, helicopter, land-rover or even hovercraft to their chosen spot. The expeditions are a great deal more scientific and less haphazard than they were, and involve very highly trained specialists.

Increasingly, as the microscope and sophisticated scientific equipment have taken the place of porters and mule, botanical exploration takes place in laboratories. In the herbariums of museums and botanic gardens all over the world, millions of dried plant specimens and their attached field notes are being scrutinized for any hint that might reveal a new drug or food source, so that the seeds can be collected and cultivated, and thereby rescued from the threat of being wiped out by some land clearance scheme. In Britain, the Royal Horticultural Society has even launched a nation-wide hunt for rare plants still surviving in British gardens.

Modern travel has made it easier for amateur plant hunters to search for plants and reintroduce lost species, but even the gardener who stirs no further than the garden gate can play a vital part in preserving the marvellous species collected at such a cost of suffering and hardship by the plant hunters.

THE PLANTS THEY COLLECTED

The following lists are a selection of the species collected by the plant hunters included in this book. The finds of Sir Joseph Banks and Richard Spruce are not listed here because, with the exception of the chinchona collected by Spruce, they collected only herbarium specimens.

Plants collected by John Tradescant the Elder

Acanthus spinosus (bear's breeches); *Cistus monspeliensis, C. hirsutus, C. ladanifer, C. populifolius, C. crispus, C. corbariensis, C. laxus, C. albidus* (rock rose); *Cornus suecica* (dogwood); *Cytisus canariensis* (genista); *Danae racemosa; Dianthus superbus* (pink); *Gladiolus byzantinus* (sword lily); *Halimium halimifolium; Iris persica; Jasminum humile, J. grandiflorum* (jasmine); *Matthiola sinuata* (ten week stock); *Oxydendrum arboreum; Prunus laurocerasus* (cherry laurel); *Rosa muscovitica* (rose); *Rubus chamaemorus; Salix eleagnus* (hoary willow); *Syringa persica* (lilac); *Vaccinium myrtillus* (bilberry); *Veratrum album.*

Plants collected by John Tradescant the Younger

Acer rubrum (red maple); *Adiantum pedatum* (maidenhair fern); *Anaphalis margariticea* (pearl everlasting); *Asclepias purpurascens* (milkweed); *Lilium canadense* (Canada lily); *Liriodendron tulipifera* (tulip tree); *Lonicera sempervirens* (trumpet vine); *Monarda didyma, M. fistulosa* (bergamot); *Oenothera biennis; Platanus occidentalis* (plane); *Robinia pseudoacacia* (acacia); *Smilacina racemosa* (false spikenard); *Viola pubescens* (pansy); *Vitis labrusca, V. vulpina* (grape); *Yucca filamentosa* (Adam's needle).
Believed to have been collected by John Tradescant the Younger: *Aquilegia canadensis* (columbine); *Aster tradescantii* (Michaelmas daisy); *Parthenocissus quinquefolia* (Virginia creeper); *Rudbeckia laciniata* (coneflower); *Tradescantia virginiana* (trinity flower).

Plants collected by Francis Masson

Aloe dichotoma; Amaryllis belladonna (belladonna lily); *Arctotis* sp.; *Asclepias* sp. (milkweed); *Cotyledon* sp.; *Crassula* sp.; *Diosmaş* sp.; *Erica* (heath: over 86 species); *Erythrina corallodendron* (coral tree); *Euphorbia* sp.; *Gladiolus* sp.; *Ixia viridiflora; Kalmia* sp.; *Lobelia* sp.; *Massonia* sp.; *Mesembryanthemum* sp. (Livingstone daisy); *Nerine sarniensis* (Guernsey lily); *Nymphaea caerulea* (water lily); *Ornithogalum thyrsoides* (chincherinchee); *Oxalis* (nearly 50 species); *Pelargonium* (geranium: 50 species); *Portulaca* sp.; *Prunus* sp.; *Rosa* sp. (rose); *Spiraea* sp.; *Stapelia* (carrion flower: 40 species); *Strelitzia reginae* (bird of paradise flower); *Trifolium* sp.; *Trillium grandiflorum* (wake robin); *Tritonia* sp.; *Viola* sp. (pansy); *Zantedeschia aethiopica* (arum lily).

Plants collected by Allan Cunningham

Acacia pendulata, A. spectabilis, A. suaveolens (wattle); *Araucaria* sp.;

Banksia oblongifolia; Boronia sp.; *Callistris australis; Casaurina stricta; Castanospermum cunninghamii; Ceratopetalum gummiferum; Chloranthus; Eucalyptus glauca* (gum tree); *Exocarpus; Grevillea acanthifolia, G. spacelata, G. sericosa; Hibiscus* sp.; *Hakea* sp.; *Hovea celsii; Lotus australis; Malastoma banksii; Olearia dentata* (daisy bush); *Solanum laciniatum; Sophora tomentosa; Tecoma oxleyii;* orchids; peroonias.

Plants collected by David Douglas
Arbutus menziesii (madroña); *Abies nobilis,* syn. *A. procura* (noble fir), *A. grandis* (grand fir); *Acer microphyllum, A. circinatum* (maple); *Calochortus macrocarpus, C. albus, C. luteus, C. splendens; Castanopsis chrysophylla; Collomia grandiflora; Clarkia pulchella; Delphinium cardinale; Erythronium grandiflorum; Garrya elliptica; Gaultheria shallon; Helodiscus discolor, H. discolor var. ariifolius; Lonicera ciliosa* (honeysuckle); *Lupinus aridus, L. leucophyllus, L. polyphyllus* (lupin); *Mahonia aquifolium* (Oregon grape), *M. nervosa; Nemophila aurita, N. menziesii,* syn. *N. insignis* (baby blue eyes); *Paeonia brownii* (peony); *Penstemon attenuatus, P. breviflorus, P. deustus, P. fruticosus, P. glaber, P. glandulosus, P. scouleri, P. speciosus, P. venustus; Phlox longifolia; Picea sitchensis* (Sitka spruce); *Pinus contorta, P. coulteri, P. lambertiana, P. monticola, P. ponderosa, P. radiata, P. sabiniana* (pine); *Pseudotsuga menziesii (douglasii)* (Douglas fir); *Purshia tridentata; Quercus garryana* (oak); *Ribes aureum, R. cereum, R. divaricatum, R. sanguineum* (flowering currant); *Rubus parviflorus, R. spectabilis; Umbellularia californica.*

Plants collected by Robert Fortune
Abelia uniflora; Anemone hupehensis (windflower); *Caryopteris mastacanthus; Cupressus funebris* (cypress); *Clematis lanuginosa; Dicentra spectabilis* (bleeding heart); *Exochorda racemosa; Forsythia viridissima, F. suspensa fortunei; Ilex cornuta* (holly); *Jasminum nudiflorum* (winter-flowering jasmine); *Lonicera fragrantissima, L. standishii* (honeysuckle); *Mahonia bealei; Platycodon grandiflorum* (balloon flower); *Rhododendron fortunei, R. metternichii, R. obtusum, R. ovatum; Skimmia reevesiana,* syn. *S. fortunei; Spiraea japonica fortunei, S. prunifolia flora plena; Vibernum cliatum, V. macrocephalum, V. tomentosum* 'Plicatum' (Japanese snowball); *Weigela rosea.*

Plants collected by Sir Joseph Hooker
Delphinium glaciale; Juniperus wallichiana; Primula capitata, P. sikkimensis (Himalayan cowslip); *Meconopsis simplicifolia* (poppywort); *Myosotis hookeri* (forget-me-not); *Rhododendron anthopogon, R. arboreum, R. argenteum (R. grande), R. aucklandii, R. barbatum, R. campbellii, R. campanulatum, R. campylocarpum, R. candelabrum, R. cinnabarinum, R. dalhousiae, R. edgworthii, R. elaegnoides, R. essinoides, R. falconeri, R. fulgens, R. glaucophyllum* (glaucum), *R. grande, R. griffithianum, R. hodgsonii, R. lanatum, R. lepidotum, R. lindleyi, R. lancifolium, R. maddenii, R. niveum, R. pendulum, R. roylei, R. salignum, R. seruginosum, R. setosum, R. thomsonii, R. virgatum, R. vassinoides.*

Plants collected by George Forrest

Abies delavayi var. georgei (silver fir); *Berberis jamesiana, B. centifolia*
(barberry); *Buddleia forrestii, B. myrianntha, B. variabilis; Camellia
saluensis, C. cuspidata, C. reticulata; Clematis forrestii; Codonopsis farreri;
Daphne aurantiaca; Diapensia bulleyana; Dracocephalum isabellae;
Gentiana sino-ornata* (gentian); *Iris bulleyana, I. milesii, I. forrestii,
Jasminum polyanthum* (jasmine); *Leptodermis glauca; Lilium thomsonianum,
L. giganteum, L. delavayi* (lily); *Osmanthus suavis; Pieris formosa forrestii;
Pleione delavayia, P. grandiflora, P. forrestii* (orchid); *Primula beesiana, P.
forrestii, P. helodoxa bulleyana, P. littonii; Rhododendron araiophyllum, R.
arizelum, R. basilicum, R. bullatum, R. campylogynum, R. crassum, R.
desquamateum, R. forrestii (reptans), R. fulvum, R. giganteum, R.
griersonianum, R. habrotrichum, R. lacteum var. macrophyllum, R. leptothrium,
R. mackenzieanum, R. nerriflorum, R. oemulorum, R. plebeium, R. rubiginosum,
R. scintellans, R. sinogrande, R. souliei, R. sulfureum, R. supranubium,
R. taliense, R. trichocladum, R. zaleucum.*

Plants collected by Ernest Henry Wilson

Acer davidu, A. griseum (maple); *Actinidia chinensis* (Chinese gooseberry);
Ampelopsis chaffanjonii, A. micans; Artemisia lactiflora (white mugwort);
Berberis julianiae, B. sargentiana, B. wilsoniae, (barberry); *Catalpa fargesii;
Ceratostigma willmottiana; Clematis armandii, C. montana rubens, C. wilsonii;
Corylopsis veitchiana, C. willmottiae; Daphne genkwa, D. retusa; Davidia
involucrata* (dove tree); *Deutzia longogolia; Euonymus sanguineum* (spindle
tree); *Hamamelis mollis* (witch hazel); *Hydrangea xanthoneura; Ilex pernyi*
(holly); *Jasminum primulinum (J. mesnyi)* (jasmine); *Kolkwitzia amabilis*
(beauty bush); *Ligularia clivorum, L. wilsoniana; Lilium davidii var.
willmottiae, L. leucanthum chloraster, L. regale; Liriodendron chinense;
Loropetalum chinense; Lonicera maackii podocarpa, L. nitida, L. pileata
L. tragophylla* (honeysuckle); *Magnolia delavayi; Malus theifere (Malus
lupehensis)* (crab-apple); *Meconopis integrifolia* (poppywort); *Paeonia obovato
var. willmottiae* (paeony); *Parthenocissus thomsonii* (Virginia creeper);
Philadelphus subcanus (mock orange); *Primula cockburniana; P. wilsonii;
Prunus dielsiana; Quercus aquifolioides* (oak); *Rosa moyesii, R. omiensis, R.
sinowilsonii, R. willmottiae; Salix magnifica* (willow); *Sargentodoxa cuneata;
Sorbus megalocarpa; Vibernum henryi; Weigela rosea.*

Plants collected by Reginald Farrer

Androsace mucroifolia (rock-jasmine); *Anemone farreri* (windflower);
Aster kansuensis (Michaelmas daisy); *Berberis dasystachya* (barberry);
*Buddleia alternifolia, B. davidii; Deutzia alba; Gaultheria trichophylla;
Geranium pylzowianum, G. sanguineum* (crane's bill); *Gentiana hexaphylla,
G. farreri* (gentian); *Incarvillea variabilis var. przewalski; Iris ensata;
Juniperus coxii* (juniper); *Lilium duchartrei, L. ochraceum* (lily); *Lonicera
farreri* (honeysuckle); *Meconopsis quintuplinervia, M. prattii, M. psilnonmma*
(poppywort); *Nomocharis basilissa, N. farreri, N. ruxantha var. imberis;
Primula burmanica, P. fasciculata, P. limnoica, P. loczii, P. scopulorum,
P. silvia, P. sonchifolia, P. viola-grandis (Omphalogramma farreri); Rodgersia*

aesculifolia; Potentilla fruticosa (cinquefoil); *Rhododendron aiolosalpinx,
R. caloxanthum, R. cerinum, R. heptamerum, R. invictum, R. oulotrichum,
R. phoenicodum, R. reginaldii, R. sperabile, R. tapeinum; Rosa farreri var.
persetosa* (rose).

Plants collected by Frank-Kingdon Ward

Acer wardii (maple); *Androsace wardii* (rock jasmine); *Berberis hookeri,
B. hypokerina* (barberry); *Cardamine verticillata; Cornus chinensis;
Cyananthus wardii; Dracocephalum hemsleyanum* (obedient plant);
*Gaultheria wardii; Gentiana atuntsiensis, G. gilvostriata, G. trichotoma,
G. wardii* (gentian); *Leycesteria crocothyrsos; Lilium arboricola, L. mackliniae,
L. wardii* (lily); *Lonicera hildebrandiana, L. tsarongensis* (honeysuckle);
Meconopsis betonicifolia var. baileyi (Himalayan blue poppy), *M. rubra,
M. violacea, M. wardii* (poppy); *Pedicularis atuntsiensis, P. pseudo-ingens;
Primula agleniana var. thearose, P. baileyana, P. cawdoriana, P.
clutterbuckii, P. deliensis, P. florindae, P. latisecta, P. melanodonta, P.
melanops, P. morsheadiana, P. normaniana, P. rubra, P. vernicosa; Prunus
cerasoides var. rubra; Rhododendron calsiphila, R. cerasinum, R. chrysolepsis,
R. closhongense, R. concinnoides, R. crebreflorum, R. curvistylum, R. forrestii
var. repens* 'Scarlet Pimpernel' and 'Scarlet Runner', *R. hirtipes, R.
imperator, R. kasoense, R. leucaspis, R. macabeanum, R. maddeni, R.
magacalyx, R. mahoganii, R. perantum, R. pruniflorum, R. riparum, R.
scopulorum, R. taronense, R. tsangpoense, R. wardii; Saxifraga wardii;
Thalictrum diffisiflorum.*

Plants collected by Joseph Rock

Paeonia suffruticosa 'Rock's variety' (paeony); *Picea asperata, P. likiangiensis
var. purpurea* (fir); *Rhododendron chryseum, R. fletcheranum; Teraktogenos
kurzii.*
Rock collected the seed of some five hundred rhododendron species, but
virtually all of them had already been collected by other hunters. The bulk
of his collections was a huge mass of herbarium material.

SELECT BIBLIOGRAPHY

Allen, Mea, *The Tradescants* (Michael Joseph, London, 1964)

Allen, Mea, *The Hookers of Kew 1785-1911* (Michael Joseph, London, 1967)

Allen, Mea, *Plants that Changed our Gardens* (David & Charles, Newton Abbot, Devon, 1974)

Banks, Joseph, *The Endeavour Journal*, ed. J. C. Beaglehole (The Public Library of New South Wales, in association with Angus and Robertson, Sydney, 1962)

Bretschneider, E., *A History of European Botanical Discoveries in China* (London, 1898)

Britten, James, 'Francis Masson', *The Journal of Botany, British and Foreign*, Vol. 22 (1884)

Blunt, Wilfred, *The Compleat Naturalist – a Life of Linnaeus* (Collins, London 1971)

Cameron, H. C., *Sir Joseph Banks* (The Batchworth Press, London 1952)

Carsten, Mia K., 'Francis Masson, a gardener-botanist who collected from the Cape', *The Journal of South African Botany*, Vol. 24 part 3 (July 1959), part 4 (October 1959); Vol. 26 part 1 (January 1960); and Vol. 27 part 1 (January 1961)

Carter, H. B., *Sir Joseph Banks and the Plant Collections from Kew Sent to the Empress Catherine II of Russia 1795*, Bulletin of the British Museum (Natural History) Historical Series, Vol. 4, no. 5 (London 1974)

Coates, Alice M., *The Quest for Plants – a History of the Horticultural Explorers* (Studio Vista, London, 1969)

Cooper, R. E. (ed.), George Forrest VMH (The Scottish Rock Garden Club, Edinburgh, 1935)

Cowan, Dr J. Macqueen (ed.), *The Journeys and Plant Introductions of George Forrest VMH*, Royal Botanic Garden, Edinburgh, staff, and E. H. M. Cox (Oxford University Press, Oxford, 1952)

Cox, E. H. M., *Farrer's Last Journey – Upper Burma 1919-1920* (Dulau & Co., London, 1926; reprint by Theophrastus Publishers, Rhode Island, New York, 1977)

Cox, E. H. M., *The Plant Introductions of Reginald Farrer* (1930)

Davies, John, *Douglas of the Forests* (Paul Harris Publishing, Edinburgh, 1980)

Douglas, David, *Journal* (Royal Horticultural Society, London, 1914)

Farrer, Reginald, *On the Eaves of the World* (Edward Arnold, London 1917)

Farrer, Reginald, *The Rainbow Bridge* (Edward Arnold, London, 1921)

Forbes, Vernon S., *Pioneer Travellers of South Africa. A geographical commentary on routes, records, observations and opinions of travellers at the Cape 1750 to 1800* (A. A. Balkema, Cape Town and Amsterdam, 1965)

Forrest, George, articles in *Gardener's Chronicle* (London, May 1910 and October 1917)

Forrest, George, article in the *Royal Horticultural Society Journal* (London, 1915, 1916 and 1924)

Fortune, Robert, *Three Years' Wanderings in China* (The University Press, Shanghai, 1935)

Gorer, Richard, *The Growth of Gardens* (Faber and Faber, London, 1978)

Gregory, J. W. & C. J., 'The Alps of Chinese Tibet and their geographical relations', *The Geographical Journal*, Vol. LXI, no. 3 (London, March 1923)

Hagen, Von, Victor W., *South America Called Them* (The Travel Book Club, London, 1949)

Hepper, F. Nigel (ed.), *Royal Botanic Gardens Kew, Gardens for Science and Pleasure* (Her Majesty's Stationary Office, 1982)

Hillier's Manual of Trees and Shrubs (David & Charles, Newton Abbot, Devon, 1973)

SELECT BIBLIOGRAPHY

Hooker, Sir Joseph, *Himalayan Journal* (Ward, Locke & Co., London, 1905)

Hooker, Sir Joseph, unpublished letters and journals, Royal Botanic Gardens Library, Kew

Kellner, L., *Alexander von Humboldt* (Oxford University Press, Oxford, 1963)

Kingdon-Ward, Frank, *The Land of the Blue Poppy* (Cambridge University Press, Cambridge (UK), 1913)

Kingdon-Ward, Frank, *The Mystery Rivers of Tibet* (Seeley Service & Co., London, 1923)

Kingdon-Ward, Frank, *The Romance of Plant Hunting* (Edward Arnold, London, 1924)

Kingdon-Ward, Frank, *Plant Hunting on the Edge of the World* (Victor Gollancz, London, 1930)

Kingdon-Ward, Frank, 'Blue Poppies', *Blackwood's Magazine*, no. 1563 (London, January 1946)

Kingdon-Ward, Frank, 'Earthquake', *Blackwood's Magazine*, no. 1627 (London, May 1951)

Kingdon-Ward, Frank, *Plant Hunting in Manipur* (Jonathan Cape, London, 1952)

Lee, Ida, *Early Explorers in Australia* (Methuen, London, 1952)

Lemmon, K., *The Golden Age of Plant Hunters* (Phoenix House, London, 1968)

Lyte, C., *Sir Joseph Banks* (David & Charles, Newton Abbot, Devon, 1980)

Masson, Francis, 'An Account of Three Journeys from Cape Town into the Southern Parts of Africa, undertaken for the Discovery of New Plants towards the improvement of the Royal Botanical Gardens at Kew', addressed to Sir John Pringle, Bart., FRS (Kew, November 1775)

Millais, *Rhododendrons and their hybrids* (London, 1917)

Naturalist, The, a quarterly Journal principally for the North of England, no. 919 (printed by the Yorkshire Naturalists Union, October-December 1971)

North, Marianne, *A Vision of Eden – the Life and Work of Marianne North* (Webb & Bower, Exeter, Devon, 1980)

Rock, Joseph, article in the *National Geographical Magazine* (US ed., Washington D.C., March 1922)

Rock, Joseph, *The Chaulmoogra Tree and Some Related Species : a Survey Conducted in Siam Burma, Assam, and Bengal*, US Department of Agriculture Bulletin no. 1057 (Washington D.C., 24 April 1922)

Royal Horticultural Society, instructions to Robert Fortune, 1843 (Library, Royal Horticultural Society, London)

Sandeman, Christopher, 'Richard Spruce – Portrait of a Great Englishman', *Royal Horticultural Society Journal* (London, December 1949)

Seeman, Berthold (ed.), *Journal of Botany*, (Robert Hardwicke, London, 1864)

Smith, E., *The Life of Sir Joseph Banks* (The Bodley Head, London, 1911)

Spruce, Richard, 'Report on the expedition to procure seeds and plants of *Chinchona succirubra*, or red bark tree', addressed to the Under-Secretary of State for India (Guayaquil, 12 October 1860)

Spruce, Richard, unpublished letters, Royal Botanic Gardens Library, Kew

Spruce, Richard, *Notes of a Botanist on the Amazon and the Andes* (Macmillan, London, 1908)

Spruce, Richard, notes on the Theory of Evolution, in a letter to W. Wilson, *Biological Journal of the Linnaean Society*, Vol. 10, no. 2 (London, June 1978)

Sutton, S. B., *In China's Border Provinces – The Turbulent Career of Joseph Rock, Botanist-Explorer* (Hastings House, New York, 1974)

Wilson, E. H., *Plant Hunting* (Boston, 1927)

Woodcock, Hubert B. Drysdale & Stearn, William Thomas, 'Lilies of the World', *Country Life* (London, 1950)

INDEX

189

ACKNOWLEDGMENTS

Photographs were supplied by Bernard Alfieri; Heather Angel; Ashmolean Museum, Oxford; A-Z Botanical Collection; BBC Hulton Picture Library; K.A. and G. Beckett; Pat Brindley; Linnaean Society; Royal Botanic Gardens, Edinburgh; Royal Horticultural Society; Harry Smith Horticultural Photo Collection; R. Thursby Pelham; Michael Warren. Crown Copyright pictures reproduced with the permission of the Controller of Her Majesty's Stationery Office, and of the Director, Royal Botanic Gardens, Kew.